# Welcome to
# iPad App
# Directory
★★★★★

Apple's iPad is the pioneering tablet that changed the technology market, and much of its success is down to the huge range of applications available to enhance it. While the apps that come pre-loaded on the iPad are fantastic, it's the ones you can download from the App Store that really tailor the device to your needs. We've scoured the Store for the best offerings for every possible requirement – as well as looking at some that you'll probably want to stay clear of. If you're new to the App Store, don't worry: we've selected the essential apps that you need to download now, so you can start making the most of your device in no time. Whether you're looking to keep the kids busy, pass the time with a great game or just relax with a film or some music, there are plenty of apps here to supercharge your iPad.

# iPad App Directory

★★★★★

Imagine Publishing Ltd
Richmond House
33 Richmond Hill
Bournemouth
Dorset BH2 6EZ
☎ +44 (0) 1202 586200
**Website:** www.imagine-publishing.co.uk
**Twitter:** @Books_Imagine
**Facebook:** www.facebook.com/ImagineBookazines

**Publishing Director**
Aaron Asadi

**Head of Design**
Ross Andrews

**Production Editor**
Alex Hoskins

**Senior Art Editor**
Greg Whitaker

**Art Editor**
Ali Innes

**Photographer**
James Sheppard

**Printed by**
William Gibbons, 26 Planetary Road, Willenhall, West Midlands, WV13 3XT

**Distributed in the UK, Eire & the Rest of the World by**
Marketforce, Blue Fin Building, 110 Southwark Street, London, SE1 0SU
Tel 0203 148 3300 www.marketforce.co.uk

**Distributed in Australia by**
Network Services (a division of Bauer Media Group), Level 21 Civic Tower, 66-68 Goulburn Street,
Sydney, New South Wales 2000, Australia Tel +61 2 8667 5288

Part of the

iPHONE, iPAD & ANDROID
Apps magazine
www.knowyourapps.com

bookazine series

IMAGINE
PUBLISHING

# Contents

Your guide to the best apps for the iPad

# 66
## Education & Kids
Feed young minds with fun and educational apps to keep them occupied for hours

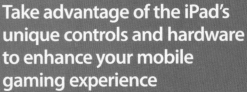

# 90
## Games
Take advantage of the iPad's unique controls and hardware to enhance your mobile gaming experience

# 120
## Creative
Use your iPad to create your next masterpiece using these original and exciting apps

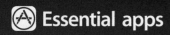 

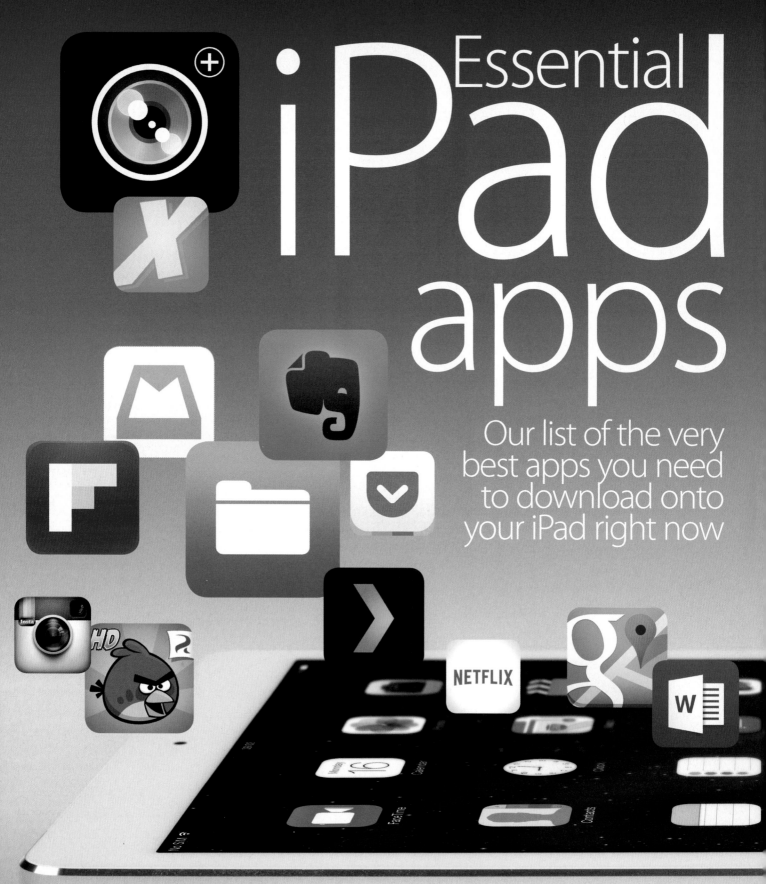

# Essential iPad apps

Our list of the very best apps you need to download onto your iPad right now

The iPad is nothing without apps. They are at the very core of Apple's tablet experience, and if you buy an iPad without installing any extra apps on it, you're really missing out on what makes the iPad so special.

With that in mind, we have worked hard to put together a list of the very best apps available for the brilliant tablet. These are all available from the built-in App Store, and the vast majority of them are available completely for free, without you needing to pay a penny.

No matter what you want to use your iPad for, there is bound to be an app you will find fun or useful in the App Store. You can complete all kinds of tasks with just a few taps of your finger. In this feature, we've rounded up the very best apps available today, in every category, so you're bound to find something in here that suits you just perfectly.

And we really have covered every base; whether you want to relax with the best new games, get your emails perfectly organised, or even just watch your favourite films on the go,

you'll find the app you're looking for in the next few pages.

Of course, we haven't just listed dozens of apps; we've also explained what it is that makes them so good, and in many cases shown you how you can use the apps to get the most from your device.

So get your iPad and your Apple ID at the ready and prepare to download the essential apps that every iPad user should own. In no time at all you'll understand exactly why the iPad is so special.

# Power up your email

## Mailbox
Price: Free

When it comes to email, sometimes the iPad's built in Mail client just isn't good enough. While it doesn't do anything particularly wrong, Mailbox is a big step up in both functionality and design.

The clean and simple look is just the start; the biggest advantage comes in the form of gestures that help you quickly sort your mail. Whether you need to deal with a message later, archive or delete it, it's just a slide away in Mailbox. It's incredibly customisable, too. The main focus, though, is getting your Inbox to zero. Move and delete your messages and you'll achieve Mailbox zen in no time at all.

## "Mailbox is a big step up in functionality and design"

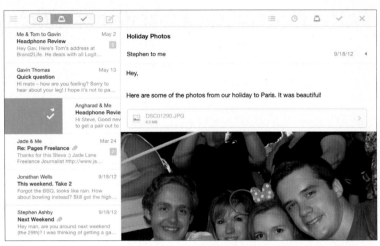

**1: Gesture based**
Swiping left and right on your messages at the side of the screen will complete different actions, and move your messages into your own custom folders, or quickly delete them.

**2: Get to zero**
The main goal of Mailbox is to help you to an empty inbox. Delete unwanted messages, save those you do need and defer others until later to completely clear out your email inbox.

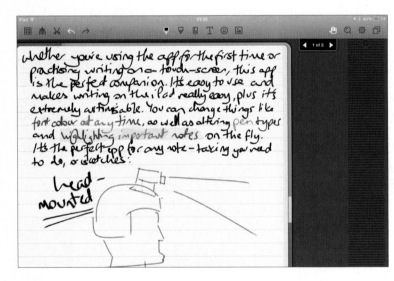

**1: Set up your page**
The app offers plenty of customisation options for your page. From paper type to pen colour and note size, you can make each notebook your own. Customise the level of zoom for the handwriting section to your needs so you're ready to go.

# Make vital notes on iPad

## Noteshelf
Price: £3.99/$5.99

When it comes to making notes, there's few things better than an iPad. While a pen and paper may always have a place in people's hearts, on an iPad you can hold hundreds of thousands of notes in one place, tag them and organise them, and correct mistakes without messing up your page. And with Noteshelf, things are even easier. Not only can you organise your notes with tags and notebooks, you can also use the handwriting feature to quickly take neat, hand-written notes. The app uses a zoomed-in section at the bottom of the screen, which allows you to write at a comfortable size, and see your notes appear smaller at the top. It's perfect to keep all your notes in one place on your device.

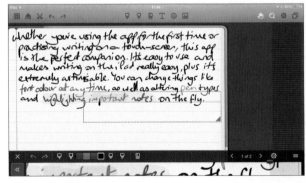

**2: Start scribbling by hand**
You can then write in the lines at the bottom of the screen and have your words transferred up to the section above. When you reach the section on the right of the box the whole thing will shift sideways to help you carry on writing unhindered.

# Take notes and projects with you

 Evernote

Price: Free

**Notes**
Every note you make is synced to your Evernote account, so they're accessible everywhere

**Sync**
Click the sync button at the top to instantly update Evernote on all your devices

**Atlas**
Allow Evernote to use location data to see your notes in an interface like iPhoto's Places

**Restore**
Tap the Trash area to restore the notes you accidentally delete in seconds

# Bookmark webpages to read later

 Pocket

Price: Free

Pocket's cross-platform bookmarking utility and minimal interface for reading your saved articles make it a firm favourite for iPad users. You can even tag articles as you save them.

**1: Save articles on the iPad**
Open Pocket on your iOS device and tap Help at the bottom of the main menu. Tap How to Save, scroll down to From Mobile Safari and tap the all-important Install button.

**2: Read your articles**
All your articles are saved to your account, and will be synced between all devices using the app. You can see all your saved articles and read them with a tap via the slick interface.

# Keep contacts together

Cobook

Price: Free

Cobook is a gorgeous app that brings together contacts in your main Contacts app on your iPad and Mac, your contacts saved in social networks and any you have in Google accounts. The UI takes cues from iOS 7, and you can tag and group contacts for even faster searching. Throw in swipe-to-call functionality and you have the ultimate in contacts syncing apps.

# Stay up to date with events

Sunrise Calendar

Price: Free

The iPad's built-in Calendar app is okay for managing a small number of events, but if you really want to take control of your life, Google's Sunrise Calendar is the app to do it. You can create events and appointments quickly and easily and even import a wide range of calendars from the initial set-up, including the fixtures of your favourite teams.

# Watch your shows wherever you are

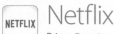 Netflix

**Price:** Requires subscription; £5.99/$7.99 per month

**Search**
Tap the search bar in the top-right to quickly find content on the Netflix service

**Personalise**
To get recommendations, and improve their quality, rate as many items as possible

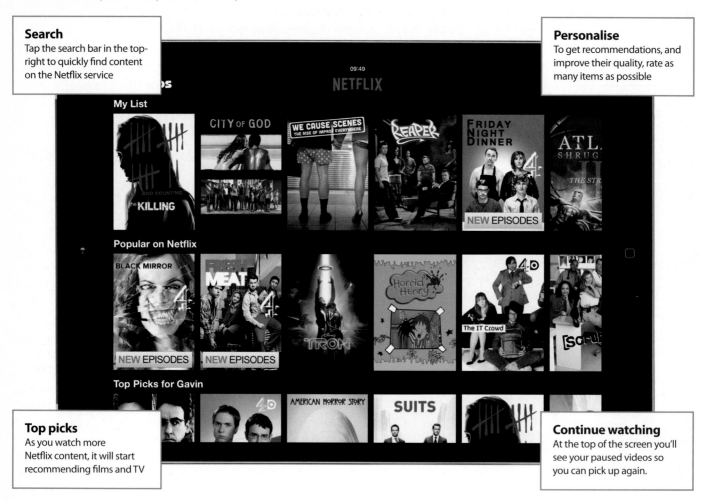

**Top picks**
As you watch more Netflix content, it will start recommending films and TV

**Continue watching**
At the top of the screen you'll see your paused videos so you can pick up again.

---

# Listen to your radio

 Spotify Music

**Price:** Free

One of the biggest names in audio streaming, Spotify is an on-demand music service. Thanks to apps for Mac, PC, Android and iOS, you can create playlists anywhere and have instant access to them on your iPad. While the service used to be paid for use on iPhone and iPad, you can now listen to your favourite tracks for free, with ads. Of course, if you want to subscribe for a paid account, you'll get the ability to download tracks to listen to offline, remove the adds, and much more.

**1: Create a playlist**
Click New Playlist in the left-hand sidebar, and give it a name. Either select from the app's featured tracks, or search for your favourites and drag them to your new playlist.

**2: Personalise your music**
Tap Settings and you'll see a number of options. You can adjust things like Gapless Playback, or activate Offline Mode if you have a paid account, so you can listen anywhere.

# Supercharge your web browser

 ## Chrome
Price: Free

Sometimes, Safari just isn't enough. If you have a Google Account and like to keep everything in sync, Chrome is the perfect app to grab for your iPad. A free add-on to your tablet, you'll be able to log in with your Google email and password and have favourites and open tabs synced between your Mac or PC and your iPad's browser.

# Video chat from any device…

 ## Skype
Price: Free

Skype has been around as a VoIP service (Voice over Internet Protocol) since way back in 2003, and these days not only supports video chats but also messaging, with full emoticon and photo support within the app. And all this is free, so it's a great option for video chats with friends and family who aren't using FaceTime. You can make audio calls for free over Wi-Fi or 4G, too, saving you credit. Not only that, you can add Skype credit to your account via your profile page and use it to make audio calls to landlines, effectively replacing your FaceTime and Phone apps. You'll need a Skype account to use it, but you can log into this account on any device, whether it's running iOS, Android, Windows or OS X.

# Control your Mac from your iPad device

 ## Screens VNC
Price: £13.99/$19.99

**1: Connect locally**
Open Screens in iOS and tap your Mac, then Save. Tap the new thumbnail and input your Mac login details – you need to be on the same Wi-Fi network.

**2: Connect from afar**
To use Screens at long range, head to edovia. com/screens and download Screens Remote for your Mac (free). Install it, create a Screens ID and sign in.

# Stay in touch with the world

 ## Twitter
Price: Free

Over the years the Twitter app has proved an effective means of communicating, spreading awareness and generally whiling away the time it takes to eat your breakfast cereal in the morning. With a simple, yet effective interface that has been upgraded and enhanced through numerous updates to be as efficient as it can be in relaying all of the latest tweets from the folk you follow and providing all the tools you need to post you own thoughts, activities and feelings as well as share links and pictures with your own army of followers. So essential that it has been integrated in your iPad's operating system, Twitter deserves to be downloaded by all.

# Adobe Creative Apps

Previously available to purchase individually or as part of the Creative Suite package, Adobe's apps are now only available with Creative Cloud (CC) membership. This means that rather than pay once to keep the apps, you must instead take out a regular subscription. Full details of the pricing plans are available to browse at adobe.com/uk/products/creativecloud/buying-guide-at-a-glance.html.

## Subscribing to Adobe Creative Cloud

**One CC app:**
**£17.58/$19.99**
per month
(annual commitment)

**All CC apps:**
**£46.88/$49.99**
per month
(annual commitment)

**All CC apps:**
**£70.32/$74.99**
Per month
(month-to-month)

## Enhance and organise photos

###  Lightroom

Lightroom for iPad requires you to have Lightroom 5 for Mac or PC, and you'll need to sign in with your Adobe CC account to get even basic use. But once signed in, any edits you make are automatically synced between devices. The editing tools are surprisingly powerful, too, and as it syncs everything you do through Adobe's Creative Cloud you can pick up where you left off on your Mac or PC.

You'll be able to edit your iPad's own photos to RAW images taken on professional DSLRs, and the app is also great for sharing your snaps from your iPad to your Lightroom library.

## Turn your photos into art

###  Photoshop Touch iOS

It's a little expensive, but this powerful editing suite offers a number of extra controls that you don't find in apps like iPhoto. Alongside the most standard editing options like Contrast and Brightness controls you'll also see that Photoshop Touch offers full layer controls. Whether you want to edit a photo or start from scratch and create a drawing of your own using your finger or a stylus, Photoshop Touch gives you all the tools you need, wrapped up in an easy-to-understand interface. Well worth a look.

## Create vector illustrations

###  Adobe Ideas

Much like Photoshop Touch, you can use Adobe Ideas without a CC account. However, sign in and you unlock the ability to sync your creations with Illustrator CC, so you can turn your quick iPad sketches into fully realised vector artwork on your desktop. The key advantage here is that with Adobe Ideas on iPad, you have support for the biggest styluses – the Adonit Jot Touch 4 and Jot Script, Wacom Intuos Creative and the Pogo Connect – which means you can draw digitally by hand on the go.

# Stream your media to iPad at home

 ## Plex for iPad & Plex Media Server
Price: £2.99/$4.99

Plex is perfect for all your media, though we particularly like it for streaming movies and TV episodes. There's a little more to set up than the other apps we're looking at here, as you'll need an app for your Mac or PC as well as the iOS counterpart, but once you're up and running you'll be able to keep all your media on your main Mac and stream to your other devices, no matter where you are. Plex is also great because it automatically gives media beautiful artwork, information and descriptions, even if they aren't included in the original files. It's a great way to watch movies and TV shows on your touch-screen.

**1: Plex Media Server**
Click Plex Media Server's menubar icon and choose Media Manager to go to its web interface. Use the '+' button to add folders on your Mac or PC.

## "Plex is perfect for all your media"

**2: Set up the Sync**
Put Plex on your iPad and connect to your server (Media Manager needs to be running). You'll now have access to all the media on your computer.

**3: Beautiful media**
Plex will look up artwork for your movies and music to create a beautiful view of your movies. Tap one and it'll stream from your Mac or PC instantly.

# Put a library in your pocket

 ## Kindle
Price: Free

 ## Zinio
Price: Free

Grab the free app from the App Store and you can read all your favourite ebooks on the go. You'll need an Amazon account, but all your bought books will sync automatically.

You can also get hold of a huge range of magazines and bookazines via Zinio. Whether you want to subscribe or just pick up a single issue of your favourite mag, it's a great option.

# Sync all your files and folders

 ## Dropbox
Price: Free

**1: Create folders**
Tap the elipsis button in the top of the Dropbox sidebar, then select Create Folder from the menu to add a folder inside the one you're viewing now.

**2: Add photos**
Tap the elipsis button again and select Upload from the top of the menu. Tap the images you want to add to your dropbox, then tap Upload above.

**3: Photos View**
Tap the Photos tab at the bottom of the sidebar to see all of your uploaded shots in a grid. Tap on any one for a full-size preview on the right of the screen.

**4: Favourites**
When you're viewing a large preview of the file you like, tap the Star icon in the top-right of the entire screen to add it to your favourites so it's easier to find.

**5: Open files in selected apps**
Some files, such as PDFs and Microsoft Word documents, can be opened in other apps for proper viewing or editing. Tap the Share button and tap Open In…

# Take Gmail with you

## Gmail
Price: Free

If you are one of the millions of people who use Gmail as their primary email service, the iPad app is sure to please. All your mailboxes and contacts from your gmail account will be synced across to your iPad automatically, and you'll get the same bright, easy-to-understand interface that you're used to across all of Google's services. Other apps may require complex setup to get your Gmail mailboxes to sync properly, but with the official Gmail app you'll be up and running in no time at all. Grab the Gmail app and take true control of your emails, whether you're on your computer or your iPad.

## "Mailboxes and contacts will sync across to your iPad"

### 1: Writing messages
Tap the red Compose button at the top of the message list to open up a new message. Here you can attach photos, add contacts from your iPad Contacts, and tap send in the top-right.

### 2: Sorting and starring
If you want to be able to find certain messages quickly, just tap the Star icon next to the message in the sidebar to favourite a message, then you can choose the Starred section to see them all together.

---

# Stay in touch with friends

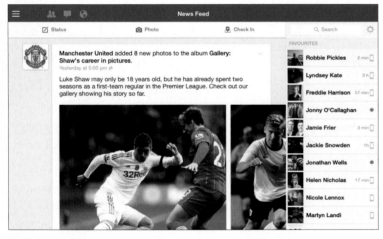

### 1: Get the app & log in through Settings
You can quickly download the app from the app store without searching by opening the Settings app and choose the Facebook section. Here, tap Install to add the app, then return to the Settings and enter your password to log into your account.

## Facebook
Price: Free

It might well be one of the first apps that many users install when they first get a new iPad, and it really is absolutely essential. If you want to keep in touch with your friends and family, there are fewer better ways than via Facebook. For many years, the official Facebook app for the iPad wasn't really very good, with slow loading times and lots of bugs. Recently, though, things have really improved, and now the app is the perfect place to see your friends' photos, what they're up to and update everyone with your latest exploits.

There is also Facebook integration built right into the iPad's operating system. Log into your account on the iPad and you can quickly share things to your own Facebook page without opening up the app. It's the perfect way to stay in touch.

### 2: Start sharing from any app
Now that your Facebook account is activated, you can share things from all kinds of locations. For example, tap the Share button in Safari and you can post a link on your Facebook wall, or do it in the Photos app to upload a shot you've just taken.

# Never get lost again

 Google Maps
Price: Free

**Aerial view**
Tap the three lines to open this menu and hit Satellite for real photos overlaid onto the map

**Location information**
Search for a location and tap the search result to see more information about it

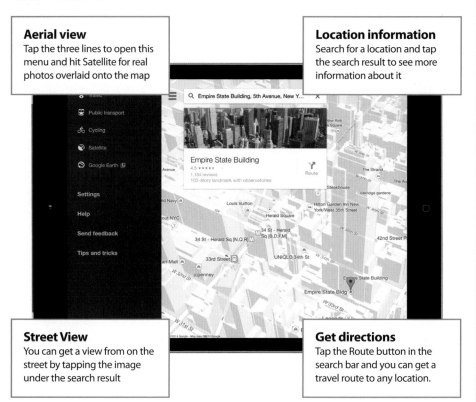

**Street View**
You can get a view from on the street by tapping the image under the search result

**Get directions**
Tap the Route button in the search bar and you can get a travel route to any location.

---

# Share your photos with the world

Instagram
Price: Free

Although Instagram, strangely, doesn't yet have its own iPad app, you can download the iPhone version that works just fine on the bigger screen. Here we show you how to start following folk…

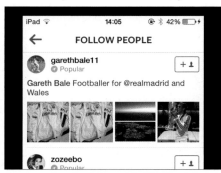

**1: Go to your profile**
Tap on the right-most icon at the bottom of the interface followed by the cog icon in the top-right corner of the screen. Now select the 'Find People to Follow' option.

**2: Connect and follow**
You can use the Connect to Facebook and Connect Contacts options to find your friends on the service or scroll down for more general suggestions and trends.

# Keep control of music and TV

 Remote
Price: Free

One of the things the iPad does brilliantly is play your media, such as movies and music. But sometimes you want to use your computer or Apple TV to enjoy your movies and music, which is where Remote is useful. It will connect to your computer's iTunes app, or your Apple TV, and act as a remote control to choose tracks or movies, adjust volume, and go full-screen.

---

# Gather inspiration

 Pinterest
Price: Free

Pinterest is like a handy online scrapbook into which you can gather the things that interest you from around the web. This is ideal if you are planning to redecorate your house and want to compile a host of styles to inspire you. Or perhaps you want a new tattoo; here you can collect designs on which to base yours. Whatever the theme, Pinterest lets you gather ideas easily. Your collections will also helpfully sync across devices.

# Get organised and share tasks

 Wunderlist: To-Do Lists & Tasks
Price: Free

**Your lists**
All of your lists will be stored here for you to tap on and view the various tasks within

**To-do lists**
Tap on the 'Add an item…' field and you'll be able to add a new to-do to your list

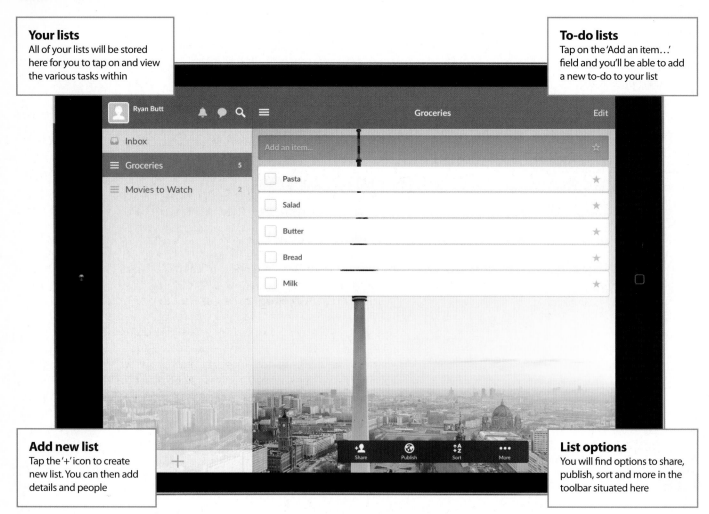

**Add new list**
Tap the '+' icon to create new list. You can then add details and people

**List options**
You will find options to share, publish, sort and more in the toolbar situated here

---

# Watch live TV

 TV Catchup
Price: Free

The iPad is perfect for watching your favourite shows. Plug in a pair of headphones and you have a personal and portable TV as thin as a notebook. TV Catchup is a brilliant service that allows you to watch live Freeview TV channels through a wireless connection no matter where you are. Now you never need to miss your favourite show again – simply open up TV Catchup and select a channel to start watching.

**1: Choose a channel**
Tap a channel from the bar on the left-hand side and you'll see a preview of what's on now, and what's coming on soon. Tap the top choice to play the TV show live.

**2: Select the settings**
Tap the cog in the top-right and you can adjust the settings within the app. Pick your television region, and choose whether your iPad can use the app via your mobile network.

# Share any file to iPad wirelessly

 Files United
Price: £2.99/$4.99

The iPad is great for viewing all your media, from movies to photos, but sometimes getting your stuff onto your tablet can prove more difficult than it should be. While you can sync files through iTunes, syncing can take a long time, and when you just want to add a few photos, it's barely worth the effort.

That's where Files United comes in. Grab the app on both iPad and Mac, and you can simply drag and drop the files you want on your iPad into the app on your Mac. It all happens instantly over your local Wi-Fi connection, making the transfer process considerably more painless than a time-consuming iTunes sync.

**1: Get both apps**
If you want to sync your files, you'll need the app on both Mac and iPad. Alternatively, just grab the iPad app for the file management tools.

## "It happens instantly over your WiFi"

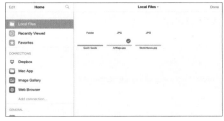

**2: Transfer wirelessly**
With both apps open, drag a file onto the app on your Mac and wait for a confirmation to appear on your iPad. Tap accept and your files will be added.

**3: Manage your files**
Once you have your files on your iPad, you can open them with a specific app, or tap Edit in the top-right and tap a file to see your sorting options.

# Create incredible photo edits

 Snapseed
Price: Free

This editing app gives you loads of powerful tools, from basic controls, like cropping and straightening, to more advanced options like vintage effects or HDR controls.

 Pixlr Express
Price: Free

Pixlr Express offers a number of editing controls, as well as creative effects, overlays, borders, text and even stickers. If you want to give your photos a new twist, it's perfect.

# Watch videos anywhere

 YouTube
Price: Free

**1: Sign in**
When you first open the app, you'll be prompted to login with your Google account. You don't have to (you can also set up a separate account) but the app will show your settings if you do.

**2: See your subscriptions**
You can tap My Subscriptions in the bar on the left to see what users you've subscribed to have uploaded, or tap an individual subscribed channel below.

**3: Search and find**
Tap the magnifying glass in the top-right of the screen to open the Search bar. Here you can type in a video title, keyword(s) or user name to find the video you want.

**4: YouTube options**
Tap the Settings cog in the top-right of the control bar and you'll be able to change all kinds of settings associated with your YouTube account, such as Wi-Fi.

**5: Upload your own videos**
You don't need the iPad YouTube app to upload your own videos; in the Photos app, simply tap the Share button and choose YouTube, then log in to do it.

# Microsoft Office for iPad

Apple's own Office-like apps – Pages, Numbers and Keynote – offer new iPad users access to powerful document tools for free, but for those that want the compatibility and tools that they're familiar with may prefer Microsoft's new Office apps for iPad. They offer plenty of functionality for free, and those with an Office365 subscription will get even more out of them, with cloud storage for your files.

## Subscribing to Microsoft Office 365

| Office 365 Home: | Office 365 Personal: | Office iPad apps: |
|---|---|---|
| **£7.99/$9.99** | **£5.99/$6.99** | **Free** |
| per month | per month | Extra features with |
| (No annual contract) | | Office 365 account |

## Create incredible documents

 ### Microsoft Word for iPad

Microsoft Word has become synonymous with word processing over the last 20 years, and now that it is finally available on iPad you'll carry all its power while you're on the move. The iPad version offers plenty in the way of document control, so you can set up your page however you like.

There is also a selection of pre-made themes that you can use to start your document, and a huge number of formatting options for your text. All of this is wrapped up in an interface that's very easy to understand and familiar to anyone with a modern version of Word. A fantastic way to work on your iPad.

## Design powerful spreadsheets

 ### Microsoft Excel for iPad

Who said you can't use the iPad for serious work? Microsoft's Excel app is perfect whether you want to put together a holiday planner and budget, or whether you need to create serious spreadsheets for your business. The chart options are as detailed as you would expect, with powerful formulas just a few taps away and graphs that look great and are very simple to create. The touch screen really breathes new life in to what is often referred to as a 'boring' app, which is a great bonus.

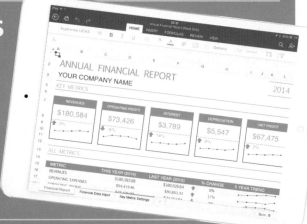

## Give amazing presentations

 ### Microsoft PowerPoint for iPad

In modern times, giving presentations to work or schoolmates has changed. Previously, adding animations and tapping the spacebar on a PC was enough to wow an onlooker, but now there is nothing cooler than swiping across a tablet as you present.

PowerPoint brings all the brilliant transitions and object animations that you remember from the PC version of the app to the iPad, along with a whole new interface that you'll get to grips with in just a few seconds. It's an incredibly powerful tool.

# Take amazing photos on the iPad

 ## Camera+ for iPad
Price: £2.99/$4.99

The built-in Camera app on the iPad is great, but there are some options that it just doesn't offer, including timed shots, stabilisation options, and a burst mode than can be activated to take multiple shots in quick succession. Camera+ does all this and more, offering powerful editing options that you can apply straight after you take a shot.

---

# Watch your favourite shows

 ## BBC iPlayer
Price: Free

The BBC offers hundreds of TV shows, and often a few films, completely free as long as you pay a TV licence in the UK. And the iPad app is the perfect way to watch these shows, wherever you are. The app uses a scrolling carousel to show you recent shows, popular options, and featured programs. Tap any one and you can watch it, ad-free, right away.

What makes the app brilliant is the sheer number of excellent programs available to watch. From big-name blockblusters like Sherlock and Doctor Who, to films that have recently aired on a BBC channel, there's plenty of choice. And with an easy-to-use interface and great options to subscribe to a series you love or download shows, it's an essential app.

## "What makes it brilliant is the sheer number of shows"

# Read amazing comics digitally on your iPad

 ## Comics
Price: Free

**1: Download your favourites**
Find comics in the Search tab, and tap In Cloud to add previously bought comics, but to purchase go to the ComiXology site in Safari.

**2: Viewing options**
When you've got an issue you want to read, you can swipe between pages as you would expect, or double-tap a single panel so it fills the whole screen.

---

# Create your own digital magazine

 ## Flipboard
Price: Free

Flipboard is a digital platform that allows you to create your own magazine based on the topics and websites you love. When you first start with the app, you can add your own Facebook and Twitter feeds if you wish, and then choose topics that interest you so they can be added to your account. From here you'll see a grid of your chosen subjects, and you can tap one to be taken to the big stories in that topic. From here, tap the '+' button in the bottom-right to create your own personalised magazine, which will be laid out beautifully for you to catch up with later or read immediately as you wish. It's the exact content you want, presented perfectly.

# Burn some rubber

## Asphalt 8
Price: Free

When it comes to gaming on the iPad, few titles manage the same high-octane, high-speed thrills that Asphalt 8 manages. Pick one of the 56 licenced cars and leap into a race, either as part of the offline career, or online against your friends, or strangers.

The latest in the Asphalt series adds aerial action to the racing, allowing you to pop 360-degree turns or barrel rolls as you work to get into first place. You can control your cars either by tilting the iPad, or with customisable touch-screen controls. Either way, this is an action-packed thrill ride that will keep you playing.

## "An action-packed thrill ride that will keep you playing"

### 1: Car choices
There are 56 cars that you are able to buy within the game, including impressive powerhouses from names like Lamborghini and Ferrari. You'll have to work hard to unlock them, however.

### 2: Ready, Set, GO
The race is incredibly intense once it starts; you'll be bumping opponents left and right, boosting whenever you've managed to build up enough, and pulling off some huge stunts whenever you come to a ramp.

---

# A beautiful and taxing puzzler

## Monument Valley
Price: £2.49/$3.99

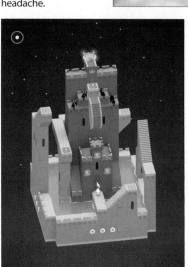

This brilliant and beautiful puzzle title takes its inspiration from the 'impossible' optical illusions you may have seen before. Each level gives you the goal of guiding a silent princess to the exit by revealing hidden pathways, unfolding optical illusions to make them into safe passageways, and outsmarting the enigmatic crow people. The game looks incredible, offering colourful worlds and a

stunning art style. While most puzzle titles will have you assessing each level when it first appears, Monument Valley will have you scratching your head every time. The first levels are easy, but the difficulty ramps up later and solving each level is a real achievement.

It's hard to explain what makes Monument Valley so special, but the design alone is worth its price tag.

### 1: Simple goals
Each level has a fairly obvious end-point – usually a door or a plinth on which to place a special item. But they are all in completely unreachable locations for any normal platforming title. You need to reshape the whole landscape of the level if you want to succeed, using spinning handles or draggable sections. Just don't get a headache.

### 2: Mind-bending solutions
Each level comes with sections which you can grab to rotate. Sometimes you'll need to spin the whole thing around to change the angle, and doing so will transform impassable gaps into straightforward paths. Other times the path will be just that little bit more obvious, but getting to it will require a little more thought than simply tapping the exit.

# A new twist on a classic genre

 ## Hitman GO
Price: £2.99/$4.99

**Board games**
The whole game is designed as a board game, with each character a piece in the game

**Sneaky sneaky**
You must sneak past guards and other obstacles to reach your target or goal

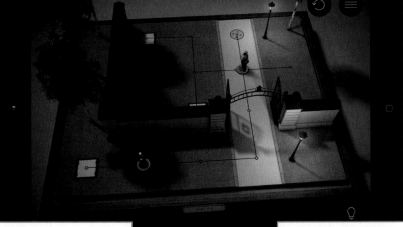

**Missions**
There are plenty of missions for you to get your teeth into, so you'll be playing for weeks

**How did you do?**
At the end of each level you'll be rated, giving the game some real replay value

# Projectile puzzling at its finest

 ## Angry Birds HD
Price: £1.99/$2.99

Angry Birds HD has been an iOS stalwart for years and comes rammed full of challenging levels. Just in case you have been living on a different planet, here's how the gameplay works…

**1: Pick a level**
Choose a level pack and then use the catapult to launch the arsenal of birds at the pig-populated structures over to the right. Different birds have different abilities.

**2: Ramp up those points**
The aim is to get three stars on every level and the amount of stars you get relates to how many points you score. Clear the level with as few birds as possible to earn the big points.

# Escape the system

## République
Price: Free

République is a tense stealth game in which you help a young woman escape her captors. You watch the action through a series of CCTV cameras, distracting guards and picking up evidence as you go. The story is engrossing and you'll find yourself exploring levels just to find the extra newspaper and notes that give the plot some background.

# Addictive adding

## Threes!
Price: £1.49/$1.99

If you want a title that will draw you in and keep you there, Threes! is the one for you. The aim is simple enough; combine two numbers of the same value to create a larger number, and keep doing this to get the highest possible number, or you run out of space. It's easy to learn but incredibly tough to master, with only a handfull people in the world having gotten every number. An addictive time-waster.

# Entertainment

## Take charge of your free time with these iPad apps

"With the right apps it's easy
to turn your iPad into an
exciting media hub"

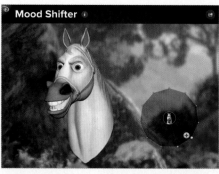
**Mood Shifter**

■ Practical exercises, such as controlling this horse's facial expression, help you hone your animating skills

■ See how lighting plays a crucial part and discover the many stages of refinement for each frame

Walt Disney understood better than anyone how important a strong story was to making a good movie. Hear him talk about it in this clip from 1956.

● Price £6.99/$9.99

# Disney Animated

## Learn the secrets of animation from the master

### PROS/CONS

▲ A thorough guide with fun, practical exercises

▲ Hours of interactive Easter eggs to enjoy

▼ Moving text can grow tiresome

▼ Some elements felt purely self-promotional

Just as they have brought countless still images to life on the silver screen, Disney has now sprinkled their magic over this comprehensive guide to animation. Designed exclusively for the iPad, Disney Animated uses hours of video clips, interactive features and practical exercises to take you through every step of producing a cartoon classic. Drawing on the filmmaker's iconic collection, the app's many behind-the-scenes features will also appeal to fans of the House of Mouse.

Framed as a breezy guide to animation, Disney Animated includes overviews of Walt Disney's approach to everything from developing a story to visual effects and adding a film score. The language used is broad rather than technical, so consider this Animation 101 rather than a step-by-step guide to making the next Cinderella or WALL-E.

However, there are also a bunch of practical activities to test your animating skills: make a ball bounce, adjust the face of a horse to convey expressions and create your own animated sequence. The latter is a simplified version of real Disney Studios software and involves both adjusting the joints of a CGI model to make them assume positions and recording it and editing the order of frames to produce a short film.

The guides themselves are illustrated with hand-drawn sketches, work-in-progress computer-generated scenes and rotating artefacts from the locked vaults of The Walt Disney Animation Research Library. Tapping on objects can trigger video cut-scenes or allow you to pinch-zoom in on images and view additional annotations. These details give the app mass appeal beyond wannabe future animators to all film lovers.

Perhaps the biggest fan service in the app is the timeline of all 53 Disney animated movies ranging from Snow White and the Seven Dwarves back in 1937 right up to the new release Frozen.

Each entry includes a plot synopsis, 'did-you-know' factoids, video clips for all major characters, cinema trailers and extracts from the musical score. The Timeline also includes key moments both in the history of Disney as a business, ranging from the opening of Disneyland in 1955 to the purchase of Lucasfilm in 2012, as well as offering some of the wider historical context of their work, such as the Great Depression and the invention of the World Wide Web.

## "Disney Animated includes overviews of Walt Disney's approach to everything from developing a story to visual effects"

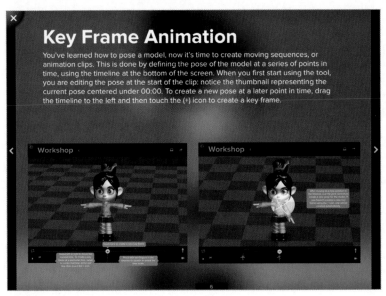

## Key Frame Animation

You've learned how to pose a model, now it's time to create moving sequences, or animation clips. This is done by defining the pose of the model at a series of points in time, using the timeline at the bottom of the screen. When you first start using the tool, you are editing the pose at the start of the clip: notice the thumbnail representing the current pose centered under 00:00. To create a new pose at a later point in time, drag the timeline to the left and then touch the (+) icon to create a key frame.

■ Included among the animation lessons are titbits of Disney's history

Each film also includes a Color Map, a unique way of viewing entire movies from beginning to end, highlighting the tones and hues that dominate each scene. Hold your finger over the multi-coloured lines to view individual frames from each film. There is also shortcut on the main menu to view the colour map for every film at once. Again, this is a feature aimed at those interested in learning the secrets behind Disney's magic, and is a great way of spotting style trends. For example, why was the colour palette of Disney's movies darker between 1980 and 2000?

All in all, this app is packed with hours of entertainment with guides divided up into chapters so that you can easily dip in and out of them. While the make-your-own-animation Workshop feature will keep bringing users back time and time again as their skills improve, so will the hunt for interactive Easter eggs.

Produced by Disney in collaboration with Touch Press, who have developed many other popular interactive books (Barefoot World Atlas, The Orchestra and March of the Dinosaurs), Disney Animated raises the bar in terms of interactivity levels. It seems like every

object on the screen has an additional function, whether it is a tapable image caption or a video clip. However, perhaps the animated text is a bit too much. While being able to drag every item on screen is fun, having the text move as well every time your finger strokes the touchpad can be very distracting when you're trying to read, annoying even, after the fourth or fifth time it happens.

A word of caution to parents, while the App Store lists this Disney product as suitable for ages four and over because it contains no objectionable material, it may be that it is a little too complicated for children under ten-years-old without supervision. Users should also be aware that all those video clips and interactive features will eat up 1.78GB of your storage – not unusual for an interactive book, but still more than your average download. Despite that, this is a brilliant app that will likely appeal to enchanted children and interested adults alike.

**Inside knowledge from the iconic film studio, completed with some great interactivity.**

## Showcase
# Get a Walt Disney masterclass

**01: 12 Principles**
Taken from The Illusion of Life book, the techniques necessary for creating cartoons – such as drawing and timing – are explained here with some helpful examples.

**02: In-depth guides**
From writing a story to creating visual effects – even creating end credits – the app is packed with Disney insights into creating an animated film.

**03: Workshop**
Head to the Workshop to get a feel for CG animation by controlling a moving puppet, playing with facial expressions, and animating a bouncing ball.

**04: Colour maps**
In this unique method of looking at the colour palette used in a film, you can view every frame of every Disney movie ever made shrunk to fit in a single page for comparison.

**05: Timeline**
This feature will probably have the most appeal to fans; view all the Disney films in chronological order with synopses, fun facts, original trailers and film scores.

**06: Elsa's snow**
The most child-friendly feature and the one that felt most like self-promotion, you can draw swirls of snow using graphics taken from the recent Disney movie Frozen.

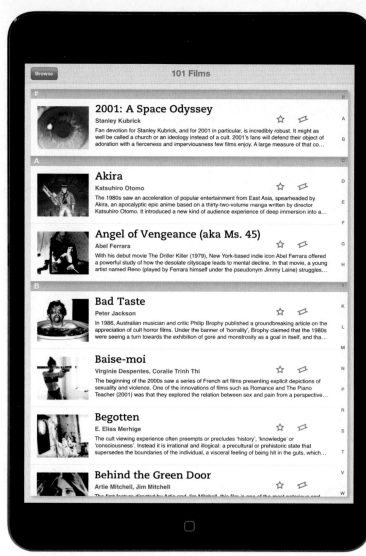

■ Browse movies by categories such as genre or directors, or make your own lists of films

■ Lots of text contextualises and discusses each film and the menu has plenty of search options

● Price £2.99/$4.99

# 100 Cult Films

## The BFI guide us through some of cinema's most amazing films

### PROS/CONS

▲ A compelling body of work that contextualises film

▲ Searching through the films is made as easy as possible

▼ Video quality can be quite inconsistent and occasionally grainy

▼ Not all film features are available for every movie

The British Film Institute is one of the film industry's most respected organisations and here it presents 100 iconic movies, selected for being interesting and influential. Drawing on the acclaimed book of the same name, with all of its insight and discussion about the various included films, 100 Cult Films: BFI Screen Guides gives the original work a multimedia twist by including film trailers and video clips.

When watched through the app, some of the videos lose their sound and picture quality, but luckily there is a button that directs you to YouTube, where the reproduction appears to be better (you also benefit from being able to read comments from other users too). Still, this isn't too much of a problem since the videos serve mainly as additions to the star attractions: the prose and the choice of films.

Dirty Dancing and Dawn of the Dead sit alongside The Big Lebowski and Fight Club. Tapping on one of these entries shows you film credits, fan sites and quotes and you can view the year it was made and its running time. Each entry can also be shared via email, Twitter and

Facebook and then be marked up as having been seen by yourself or as something you want to watch another day. Its strength lies in its searching abilities and the fact you can not only view and edit films you've seen and browse your favourite flicks, but also search by director, year of release and genre, jumping through the list using the alphabetical menu that runs down the side of the screen. There is no doubt that this is an impressive body of work made even better by clear presentation.

Other elements of the app are present but do not overwhelm or detract from the central message, instead enabling you to get more out of the information that is presented to you.

For film fans, BFI's 100 Cult Films is an essential purchase and a guide that you will no doubt return to again and again for both reference and inspiration.

**A beautiful guide to some of history's most wonderful films written in an engaging and thought-provoking style.**

● Price **Free**

# Beyond The Screen

### Enjoy another bite of the Cornetto Trilogy

 Are you a fan of the films Shaun of the Dead, Hot Fuzz and The World's End? Well. you can now get the inside scoop on the movies known as the Three Flavours Cornetto Trilogy with this free download. Beyond The Screen is packed with trivia about cameos, locations and movie references that appear in Simon Pegg, Nick Frost and Ed[...] content aside, [...] uses your iPad's mi[...] soundtrack of the film[...] facts about scenes as the[...] the Screen displays informat[...] nuggets in beautifully designed [...] animated infographics.

Any facts or figures that pop up, incr[...] the total number of pints drunk, weapons [...] used and bodies slain, can also be sent to the Freezer with a tap so you can review them later when you're not watching the film. Ideal for when the action becomes too gripping to look away.

Once the credits have rolled, there are quizzes to test your knowledge. A perfect score is hard to obtain, so the quizzes add another dimension to the app's replay value.

**A very impressive companion app that we hope to see expanded to include some other new home releases.**

★★★★☆

---

● Price **£9.99/$13.99**

# Beethoven's 9th Symphony

### Explore the best recordings of Beethoven's masterpiece

 Fans of classical music are in for a treat with this app enabling you to explore Beethoven's 9th Symphony in detail. It features four of Deutsche Grammophon's best recordings and is best experienced with earphones.

The screen is split with passage by passage notes in the top half and the score in the bottom half. As the music plays, the score cleverly scrolls in time and the explanatory notes automatically change. You can drag the score to show and play from any point or drag the play position indicator. There is the full score, a curated score, photos of the original manuscript and a modern BeatMap. There is also an

orchestra view with blobs representing the musicians and they light up when their instruments sound.

To help you explore the music, there is The Story section, which is a book on Beethoven, and a collection of video clips from experts in the Insights section. A free version of this app is available if you want to sample it before you buy, but this lite version lacks the hours of quality content the £9.99 Full Edition offers.

**A brilliant analysis of a great piece of music, but you'll want the paid version to make the most of it.**

★★★★★

■ A free version of the app is also available, but it lacks most of this [...]

...gar Wright's collection. Putting
the app's best feature is that it
...crophone to sync with the
...s to display relevant
...n unfold. Beyond
...ion as simple
...and
...uding

Rather than offering a complete collection of his numerous films (which would amount to over 135 hours of footage), this app contains clips selected by Ken himself to illustrate various themes of American history. The slick interface shows a zoomable timeline – ranging from 1776 to the present day – with circular photos representing the clips, whose colour-coded borders indicate which of the six themes they belong to. The rather short Innovation theme is free

to play, but you'll need to make an in-app purchase (£6.99/$9.99) to unlock the rest: Art, Hard Times, Politics, Race and War. The 23 documentaries are listed along the bottom of the screen; simply tap one to highlight its clips and get links to watch it on Netflix or download from iTunes.

While viewing the clips in a themed playlist doesn't offer quite the same narrative

flow as a documentary proper (despite introductions from Ken himself and some extra interviews), it does nonetheless give you a good overview of American history.

**A useful introduction to Ken Burns, although you could watch the full films on Netflix for about the same price.**

★★★★☆

---

● Price £7.99/$11.99

# Seamus Heaney: Five Fables

## Classic fable stories brought to life

Whether you have a love of literature or have a child who loves animation, the Seamus Heaney: Five Fables app is sure to become a fond favourite for all the family.

The app presents Seamus Heaney's (Irish poet, Noble Prize winner of literature and most likely author of poetry you studied in GSCE English) adaptation of Aesop's Fables by 15th Century Scottish poet Robert Henryson. The well-known tales, such as 'The Two Mice' and 'The Mouse and the Lion', have been enchantingly animated for all ages to enjoy. Billy Connolly narrates in English, while medieval expert Ian Johnson

allowing users to seamlessly switch between them.

As well as charming stories, the app has videos of leading academics including the poet reading the original and translated text, and academic notes to add context.

Five Fables was one of Heaney's last projects before his death in 2013. The price could be considered steep, but with the amount of bonus material included, it does offer good value.

**Entertainment meets education in this heart-warming and fascinating story-led animated app.**

★★★★★

■ Beautiful animation mixes with the written word

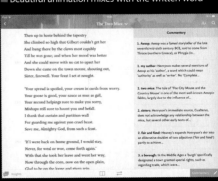

■ Users can read Seamus Heaney's translation

● Price Free

# PolyFauna

 As soon as you hear that Radiohead were involved in developing this app, you can expect something unusual. Use your phone to look around and the imagery on screen will change accordingly. Photos can be snapped from within the app and following a red dot brings more surprises.

**An immersive and unusual experience on every single level.**

★★★★★

● Price £0.69/$0.99

# Francines Voice Factory

 Following the success of Francine on Britain's Got Talent, this app offers her best impressions. Prank your friends by playing the voices on the phone or use the included ringtones. It works well, but is mostly a novelty app..

**An amusing app that fans of Britain's Got Talent will find enjoyable.**

★★★★★

● Price £2.99/$4.99

# Starting Shakespeare

 This app uses various different methods to teach the bard's basics clearly and concisely. Using humour, visual cues (including videos) and historical context, it all comes together to create a truly brilliant learning tool.

**An accessible and compelling way to teach Shakespeare.**

★★★★★

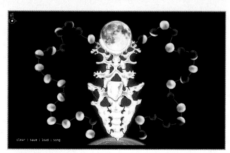

● Price £1.49/$1.99

# World Factbook

 The temptation to think that the information in World Factbook HD could be found elsewhere is huge, but that does not mean you should pass it by. The interface design, quality of the maps and information is impressive; it even works offline. A real information powerhouse.

**Country-specific information paired with pleasing design.**

★★★★☆

● Price £8.99/$12.99

# Biophilia

 You will need to be a fan of Björk to fully enjoy this title, but maybe you could also take a leap and discover her music. The idea is that the music is set to clever visuals designed for interaction. They play alongside each track using special effects and other tricks to bring the music to life. It works well and looks fantastic, but many will just prefer to listen to the music.

**A unique presentation of music that will be loved mostly by Björk fans.**

★★★★☆

● Price Free

# Fry

 What's the next best thing after Stephen Fry? A virtual version of course. It sounds bizarre and initially feels strange, but the content does work and the experience is completely original. The Headcasts are bite-sized chunks of thought from Stephen himself and they are almost always worth a quick listen. If you like the man, this app is worth checking out.

**A clever and original way to present celebrity thoughts.**

★★★★☆

■ The guide menu crawls along the bottom of the screen, but can be pulled up for easy navigation

■ Discover the types of equipment the band used to record their distinctive sound

● Price £1.99/$4.99

# The Doors

## The complete story of Jim Morrison and Co

### PROS/CONS

▲ Content and details beyond what you would ever expect

▲ Bursting with media to delight any fan

▼ Only previews of tracks

▼ Several unexplained links to external Doors site

When you are one of the most iconic rock bands ever, with a front man synonymous with headlines and controversy, you could argue that creating a content-filled app would be a fairly easy feat. Yet the amount on offer in The Doors is truly impressive, and will not only utterly delight fans, but also engage and interest those with less of a devotion to the band.

Such is the level of detail, displayed through some truly stunning digital memorabilia, even if you've never bought a Doors album before you will quickly find yourself mesmerised by the story of the band and lead singer Jim Morrison in particular. The cold hard numbers tell us that there are more than 700 images within the app, as well as over 100 sound clips,

including previews of every track from every album the band released. These are all held within themed home screens for each record, and alongside the track lists there are documents, artworks, images, scrapbooks and videos. Essentially each has its own dedicated app – themed and around that release. It's a hugely impressive archive of music and art, but incredibly this is only the beginning of this app and its contents – though you will be linked back here on plenty of occasions when exploring elsewhere.

The Story section is a very good way of bringing together a lot of the different segments of the app into a single scrollbar, with the life and times of The Doors shown in chronological order. Key tours are covered in dedicated eBooks

alongside the latest album releases – linking you back to the already mentioned sections. There's a Jim Morrison tribute section, full of writings about him from fellow band members and famous figures, such as from Rolling Stone journalist Hunter S. Thompson. The great thing about the Story bar is that it can be pulled up on any screen and swiped through, no matter how deep you find yourself elsewhere.

Functionality and design has also been given plenty of consideration, with so much content to navigate this is a big positive. The pop-up menu can be accessed on any screen and allows users to quickly skip between sections, so should you catch a reference to the band's European tour in 1968 in the timeline section, in a couple of taps and swipes you can be reading through the eBook devoted to the events of that tour. Encyclopedic would be a good way to look at the amount of

## "Here is a digital museum that stands alone in what there is to read, watch and listen to"

■ The library and galleries contain impressive extra material for fans

information and insight available to you. Perhaps the best example of this is the collection of full court papers from Morrison's infamous Florida trial in 1970, including transcripts rulings and FBI exchanges regarding Morrison and the case.

Another key function of the app is the ability to favourite any page and add it to the favourites section by tapping and holding on any given screen. This gives users the chance to create their own abridged version of the app as they explore it. For real fans of the music, the media player that first appears in the album section is actually present throughout the app, so users can listen to track previews anytime.

These are only song clips, with links to iTunes should you wish to

download the full track. On the subject of music fanatics, a hidden gem for audiophiles is Tech Nuggets' section under each album, which details every piece of equipment used by the band in the studio recording that album. It's detail on a quite incredible level, and it sits in an app alongside handwritten poetry by Morrison, old tape cases, and maps of LA showing key sites in Doors history as a band.

What we have here is a digital museum that stands alone in terms of what there is to read, watch and listen to. It is a shame that given the amount of content across the screens, full tracks can't be listened to, but you'll soon forget under the weight of other media.

If you're a Doors fan, buying this app is a no-brainer, but even for those of us with just a passing admiration will be seriously tempted to invest in something that gives you as much as this app does.

**Stunning in so many ways, this is definitely an app for audiophiles to treasure.**

■ The app includes multimedia guides to the history of the band's biggest moments

## Showcase
## Keep rocking with these features

### 01: Photos
There's a huge array of candid and immersive photography running throughout the app that offers an insight into The Doors' downtime, including in studio sessions.

### 02: Albums
Each of the band's albums has its own dedicated section, complete with lyrics, track previews and artwork. It's an impressive and cohesive collection.

### 03: Comic
A cool graphic comic, complete with actual audio clips of the now infamous Miami gig from 1969 that prompted Morrison's arrest. A unique and engaging feature.

### 04: Tech
For the serious audiophiles there is an in-depth segment dedicated to the specific equipment the band used when recording each one of their albums.

### 05: Notes
There are plenty of intimate pieces of content too, including handwritten poems and notes from Morrison, offering a different perspective on the band.

● Price £0.69/$0.99

# The Guitar Collection: George Harrison

### If you are a Beatles fan, you're in for a treat

If you are a fan of The Beatles or George Harrison, this app will likely catch your attention. If you are also a musician and have an interest in the tools great musicians use, this app will be a dream come true. The main focus is to show you the guitars Harrison used throughout his career, but the level of detail included for each model is what sets it apart.

You can view hi-res images of each guitar, zooming in and spinning them around, and the quality is stunning. Each guitar is annotated and full previews of each track the guitars were used on are a tap away. The methods used to link these parts together is natural and makes most of the competition feel clunky in comparison.

There are also detailed histories for each model and a unique 360-degree view that highlights every mark

on the original guitars used by George Harrison. As a focused history on instruments related to a particular individual, the attention throughout is always surprising.

When moving around the app you will be able to access photos and videos that have been picked for their quality, and there is a lot more here if you take the time to view the help system. It is all very natural in use and cleverly hides many features to leave the interface looking clean, but ultimately, it is a resource that will suit most people.

It will educate you, entertain and surprise you in equal measure, but true fans will delight in the way this app has been built. It's a visual and intellectual feast and the price is astonishing for the amount of content and quality on offer.

**A brilliant example of how to make a visual app that is centred around just one musician and their instrument. Virtually faultless.**

★ ★ ★ ★ ★

> "View hi-res images of each guitar, zooming in and spinning them around"

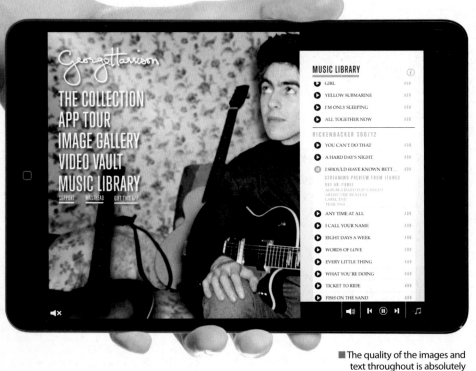

■ The quality of the images and text throughout is absolutely stunning and will appeal to fans

■ The included videos are of good quality with great entertainment value

■ Each guitar features clear annotations and useful detailed descriptions

• Price Free

# Wall Of Sound

## Play your music library via a wall of album covers

 Wall of Sound is a beautiful way to view and listen to your music collection – both stored locally and on iCloud. Upon launching, you're greeted with an attractive wall of album covers. Just click one to start playing it – if on iCloud, it may take a few seconds to start streaming. Swipe the album art of the current album to see a list of the tracks and a shuffle option. You can swipe the playing window to the top of the screen for a better view of the wall.

The app offers a different and appealing way to access your music and we found that it helped us to rediscover old tunes we'd forgotten about. By default, it shows all of your music on the wall, which you can scroll around to find more. Tapping the icon at the bottom-right brings up a menu from which you can filter the content by genre and playlist – it's possible to tick multiple choices for each. In addition, you can opt whether to include music from iCloud and any without artwork (showing a musical notes icon on the wall instead).

You can also include related music previews from the iTunes Store - another nice feature to add to the app's selling points.

**A different and visually appealing way to listen to your music and discover even more. It really is beautiful.**

★★★★☆

• Price £0.699/$1.99

# Lochfoot

## Part Bigfoot, part Nessie, lots of fun

There is no shortage of imagination in the App Store these days, thanks in part to the power of the devices that developers have to work with. Now, every single story and children's book can be brought to life and made more vivid than ever before.

Lochfoot is the perfect example of this; it's a fresh, new story that is given life as an interactive story, telling the tale of two youngsters who come across the son of the Loch Ness Monster and Bigfoot when they wander from their parents' campsite.

Though there isn't a lot of interactivity apart from tap-able speech bubbles to hear characters repeat what they said on that page, the colourful art style really does stand out and makes up for it.

There is a narration to go along with the text, which appears in short bursts, keeping the story accessible to readers of all ages. However, the narrator often lacks passion and animation in their tone, which can detract from the story and action on screen and makes things feel monotonous. It is a shame, as the animation itself is fun, and is let down by the flat narration.

Because of the short attention span of its audience, Lochfoot isn't overly long, but younger readers should still find plenty to love about this story.

**Not over-complicated but still offering plenty of fun, this makes for a fun and endearing bedtime story.**

★★★★★

■ Lochfoot: son of Bigfoot and the Loch Ness Monster

■ Speech bubbles that appear on screen can be tapped and interacted with

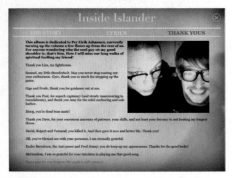

■ The lyrics and thank you section add to the album sleeve notes feel

■ Several videos are included, but you'll find most of them on YouTube regardless

● Price £13.99/$19.99

# Bernhoft Islander

## The album sleeve updated for the 21st century

### PROS/CONS

▲ Some interesting ideas here, including the option to remix a track

▲ High-quality music tracks are a welcome inclusion for audiophiles

▼ Many of the app's sections lack any real depth to them

▼ Doesn't play nicely with other music apps on your iPhone or iPad

If you're of a certain age, you'll know that downloading a handful of MP3s to your hard drive or clicking a link in Spotify isn't quite the same as opening up a CD or vinyl album, and this is Jarle Bernhoft's attempt to bring back "the true voice of the artist" to the album-making process. The Islander app is essentially his new Islander album, wrapped up with a pile of extra features and add-ons that flatter to deceive.

There's some very average fare here — the obligatory merchandise links and photo galleries are pretty ho-hum — but the 8-track mixing console and loop station are more interesting. Unfortunately there's only one track you can remix, and the loop station ends up being pretty limited too once you dig into it. On the plus side, the software design and interface is polished, and everything flows together in a nicely done carousel front-end.

It's a similar story with the Inside Islander section (a lukewarm attempt at digital sleeve notes) and the 360-degree video, which are both briefly diverting. You do get the album in high-quality 48k 24-bit HD audio (hence the hefty 1.48GB download size), which

is certainly welcome, even if you have to upgrade your speakers or headphones to notice. The trouble is, you're going to leave Rdio or iTunes every time you want a little dash of Bernhoft, which isn't ideal.

Overall, the app doesn't really fulfil its potential and feels a little half-baked. Getting the entire album helps with value-for-money, but we were looking for more exclusive content and meaty extras.

**Some decent ideas here, and the high-quality audio is to be applauded, but unfortunately it's largely disappointing.**

★★★☆☆

## "The high-quality album helps, but we wanted more exclusive content and meaty extras"

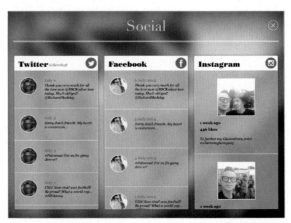

■ The social media section is a duplication of existing web content

# Sherlock: Interactive Adventure

### ...elling of a Holmes story with elementary interaction

A Sherlock Holmes app made in Russia? It turns out that the quintessential quirky English detective is very popular there. It's ...n deduced that this is no point-and-click ...re but a digital retelling of the short story 'The ...ded League' with a few interactive elements. ...ch page, the orientation of the device ...nes whether you get the book text shown ...e animation, or just the latter full-screen with ...narrated. The interactive element is limited to ...around certain 3D scenes (others are preset ...-activated animations), or zooming in – with ...ying glass, naturally – to search for objects. ...en't clues, however, and there's no way to ...e the story. Instead, found items are added ...llection screen along with interesting tidbits ...em. Similarly, locations visited appear on a ...9th Century London.

...aracters encountered are added to a dossier, ...with client Jacob Wilson, perplexed after ...ked to join the mysterious Red-Headed ...nd spend four hours a day transcribing the ...pedia Britannica. Naturally, there's an ulterior

motive, resulting in Holmes and Watson solving the mystery. Ten of the 30 scenes are free, but to unlock more you'll need to pay £1.99/$2.99.

The production values are certainly high, with real attention to detail. Highlights include a bustling street and a 3D, slow-motion action scene. Unfortunately, the app adds little to the original story, which you could read for free (in The Adventures of Sherlock Holmes).

---

**Some very high production values and a classic mystery story, but unfortunately the limited interaction is disappointing.**

★★★★★

> ...e production values ...e are certainly high, ...owing real attention ...detail"

Duncan Ross
Pablo de Sarasate
Peter Jones

An official police agent from Scotland Yard.
A big, burly man.
Imbecile in his profession, but brave as a bulldog and tenacious as a lobster.

...includes case files on all of the
...characters

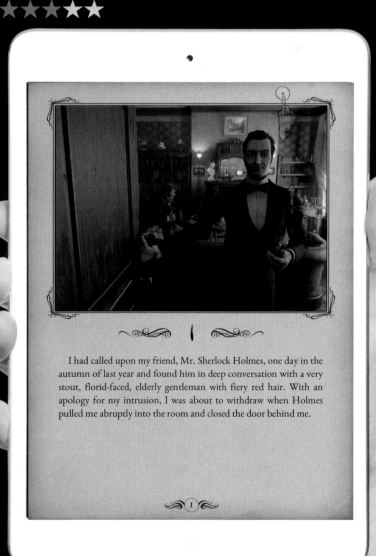

I had called upon my friend, Mr. Sherlock Holmes, one day in the autumn of last year and found him in deep conversation with a very stout, florid-faced, elderly gentleman with fiery red hair. With an apology for my intrusion, I was about to withdraw when Holmes pulled me abruptly into the room and closed the door behind me.

I

■ The use of colour is creative as pages are mainly monochrome, with splashes of colour for emphasis

● Price £0.69/$0.99

# Little Dead Riding Hood

## A twist on the classic tale in this interactive book

■ The developers have done well to twist the classic tale of Little Red Riding Hood into something new

Since the iPad's launch, it has proven itself to be a hugely popular device for reading books – and with so many inputs and sensors built into the device the interactive book market has really taken off. No longer do stories have to be limited to the written word in a glorified PDF – now they can take on a whole new form, with animated sections, interactive elements reacting to taps and shakes, and integrate sound effects and mini-movies.

Promising both a deathly and a digital twist on the classic fairytale, Little Dead Riding Hood is an interactive book that seemed to look the part right from the off. The art style used is lovely – the pages clearly started out as hand-drawn sketches

and evolved into cleaner, digitally drawn finished articles. All of the characters are beautifully realised, with unique designs that show plenty of personality. There is an Extras section that shows the creative process behind the book, which is a great addition.

The real bonus here is the ability to 'paint' over the pages with a finger and turn the sketched outlines of the characters into the finished, full-colour versions you see in the story itself. The app's music works really well with the artwork to create a spooky ambiance, giving the successful iPoe series a run for its money as the most spine-tingling interactive story.

The story itself switches regularly between a few styles with some pages remaining as simple hand-

drawn sketches on a brown paper background. You can see the individual strokes on the page and it gives the book a really raw feeling that works well as the story progresses. For the most part, though, the illustrations are done digitally; they're still clearly hand-drawn but they have real polish. The colour scheme is almost exclusively black, white and grey, with the odd colour being picked out of the page – a perfect art style is perfect for a children's book with a dark twist.

There is certainly a darker side to this story– this isn't the normal Little Red Riding Hood tale. Instead, you hear a story about how the heroine of children's fables actually died. The story revolves around how her nasty parents, who are also long-buried, are planning to poison Red Riding Hood's grandmother and spend her savings on a large tomb in which to enjoy the afterlife. Granny hears about this plan, however, and is having none of it – she arms herself with a hilarious arsenal

## "The app's music works really well with the artwork to create a spooky ambiance, giving the successful iPoe series a run for its money"

■ The narrative is quite dark for a children's story, so may scare some younger readers

and prepares to repel her skeletal granddaughter, who is ignorant of the plan. It's an excellent adaptation of the tale, although we did feel that the inclusion of the wolf was a little tacked on and not fully developed – it will surely provide some laughs for kids, but we couldn't help but feel sorry for the downtrodden wolf.

The story is narrated, with the audio beginning automatically when you turn the page. Some of these pages contain the words spoken in full, while others show no words at all. Almost every page hides some kind of animation, and you definitely get rewards for experimenting tapping around the screen. It's the perfect way to make sure kids get more involved in the story, and helps to add another layer to the tale.

■ This 'Burton-esque' story mixes a combination of pencil and digital sketches

A small team of developers made the book and the primary language for the story is Spanish. Some readers may notice a few oddly worded sentences dotted through the story for this reason, but these small translation issues do not really take anything away from the story – and it's more than likely to go unnoticed by children.

There are a few scary moments, however, and while there are comedic elements to the narrative, the undead theme probably makes this a book for slightly older readers. Still, it's a nicely formed story bursting with personality and a host of likeable and well-drawn characters. There are laughs in there for kids and adults, with lots of interactive elements and hidden gems to find. The Extras section is a great bonus, and shows how the book developed (even if the annotations are only available in the original Spanish).

A few translation issues are the only real downside to this beauty of a book and for this price you can't go wrong.

**A beautifully drawn book full of interactivity, and only a couple of translation issues.**

## Showcase
## How the story was resurrected

### 01: Extras
The Extras section lets you paint over the developer sketches to turn them into the finished characters. It's great to see the background process behind the app.

### 02: Recurring characters
A raven appears regularly throughout the story – tapping on him will often cause a funny animation or unfortunate accident to befall him.

### 03: Scares!
On some particular pages, tapping the screen will cause one of the creepy characters like Little Dead Riding Hood to suddenly leap on to the screen and scream!

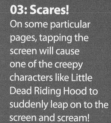

### 04: Art styles
The combination of simple sketches with more detailed digital drawings not only mixes things up, it also gives the characters more personality and adds visual interest.

### 05: Humour
Among the darkness, the story manages to be really quite funny in places – for example, Granny used to be called 'Ramba', and has a suitably ridiculous arsenal at her disposal.

Page 11 - Is A Flame A Solid, Liquid Or Gas?

**IS A FLAME A SOLID, LIQUID OR GAS?**

None of these. A hot enough flame with ionised parts can be considered a plasma. A flame is the part of a fire that we see and feel. Neither of these is a material but what produces them is, and therefore is in a particular state of matter while the flame exists. For a fire to be produced we need heat, oxygen and a fuel. When these three things are combined, a chemical reaction takes place, which produces new compounds. In the case

of wood we get charcoal and a gas made of carbon, hydrogen and oxygen. As this gas is heated it breaks down and forms new substances in the form of water, carbon dioxide, and other products. The flame produced by these gases releases energy in the form of light and heat, hence a flame. To prove these substances are a gas, scientists analyse the light from the flame using spectroscopy, which will show what elements are present.

■ Descriptions and annotations are condensed, yet informative

■ High-res imagery is one of the highlights of the app

## Special promotion

● Price Free

# Brain Dump

A dedicated digital title to answer all of your questions

### PROS/CONS

▲ Short, sharp editorial that gives you all of the facts up front

▲ Great imagery to accompany each story and that instantly engages

▼ You're perhaps left wanting more in terms of content

▼ No multimedia features as of yet

 Being inquisitive is an inherent part of human nature. Whether it be about the natural world around us or something we have created ourselves, our curiosity is what has driven most of our major discoveries and has guided us as far as travelling into space. There is nothing more satisfying than getting answers to mind-boggling questions, and this is where Brain Dump comes in. From the team behind the hugely popular How It Works magazine, this is the first digital-only magazine of its kind.

The concept here is simple: to answer all the curious questions about the universe we live in, from the smallest molecules to the biggest galaxies.

The key is that Brain Dump deals with every question in short, sharp articles, supported by eye-catching and stunning imagery. It emphasises the point nicely, and adds a definite 'wow' factor to the content. This is a Newsstand app, where users can

start a subscription, and these range in length from a single month, at the price of £0.69/$0.99, all the way up to a £3.99/$5.99 yearly subscription for 12 issues; a comparatively reasonable price scale. You can even try out the 10-page sample issue for free, giving users a flavour of what to expect.

The content, though, is the real star here, with lots of information packed into easy-to-read byte-size articles, perfect for the Twitter generation of fast consumption. There are plenty of cool infographics to keep you engaged too, and the sheer weight of facts that the magazine throws at you gives you all the ammo you could ever need down the pub to impress your friends.

**Quick and easy to read, this content-rich and visually stunning title is packed with the answers to satisfy a curious reader.**

★★★★★

To record a show, either find it in the Guide or search for it, tap 'Record This' and the information is sent to the box, even if the box is in standby mode (though it'll need up to 30 minutes to register). While it usually offers a choice of recording one episode or the whole series, we found it a bit hit and miss. You can access all the recordings on your box from the Saved Items section.

The TV Guide could be improved, though. It shows Now & Next, while swiping left brings up later shows for a single channel at a time, so it's difficult to plan your viewing. Swiping right, however, reveals earlier shows on certain channels to watch on demand.

A handier feature is the gesture-controlled playback; tap to pause, swipe left and right to rewind and fast-forward, or up and down to change channel.

**A handy remote/recording app that works well, although there are still a few issues that need ironing out.**

★★★★☆

● Price **Free**

# Freesat

## Control your Freesat box from your iOS device

This official app offers remote control and recording for Freesat and Freetime set-top boxes. This involves creating a Freesat ID on the website and entering the six-digit code from your box there. You can then use the app – via Wi-Fi or 3G/4G – to set recordings and play existing ones on the TV.

● Price **£2.99/$4.99**

# American Interior

## Multimedia game as engaging as it is quirky

American Interior is an ambitious multi-platform experience by artist Gruff Rhys, perhaps most famous as a member of the band Super Furry Animals in the 1990s. He has combined a book, film, solo album and most importantly for us, an app to tell the story of John Evans, an 18th-century explorer from Wales, who travelled to the USA in search of a mythical tribe of Welsh-speaking Indians.

The story itself is fascinating even for the casual follower of history, as it gives a new insight into life in the very young United States at the time, but the way Rhys presents it through the 100 individual chapters in the app makes it even more engaging. It is mostly a tap-and-read/listen/watch experience, but the design and storytelling craft more than make up for any lack of interactivity, and Rhys's thick Welsh accent and quirky presence make it that much more personable. If there is any complaint to be found, it is that at times it feels like a taster platter of the other versions, as you won't get full songs to listen to, chapters to read or scenes to watch, but it's only a minor drawback as we kept tapping feverishly through to the end of this quirkily epic double journey of Evans and Rhys, 200 years apart.

**Successfully combines an eclectic mix of ways to tell a lost epic of a story, and offers an engaging design.**

★★★★★

■ The maps accompany Rhys and Evans journeys

■ The beautiful artworks will surely find their way onto fans' desktops

■ The dark and gloomy graphics set the tone for an immersive story slowly unfolding

■ Bookmark any part of a chapter which catches your eye to come back and review later!

● Price Free

# Haunting Melissa

Haunting Melissa delivers chills and thrills to your iPad

## PROS/CONS

▲ Teaches you some patience – you don't know when the next chapter will appear

▲ Easy to use, with no clutter and no overuse of buttons and icons

▼ App is free but requires in-app purchases to view the content

▼ Lacks interactivity – this only comes when connecting to external sites

Haunting Melissa is the brainchild of Neal Edelstein, producer of big screen scares like the surreal thriller penned by David Lynch Mulholland Drive and nail-biting horror The Ring, and aims to revolutionise the distribution of movies on mobile devices.

It goes without saying that Haunting Melissa isn't an app in the traditional sense. In fact, it is arguable whether the app offers any features that make it, well, an app. In short, Haunting Melissa is a downloadable episodic series based around Melissa (played by Kassia Warshawski), who experiences some paranormal activity in the farmhouse that she shares with her father and the memories of her dead mother. The app comes with the first episode

(or chapter) for free, but viewing the rest of the chapters comes at a cost of either £10.49 SD/£16.99 HD for the whole season or, alternatively, you can purchase each chapter on its own for £1.49 SD/£1.99 HD.

So why is it being released as an app and not as a TV series? The whole point of Haunting Melissa is to keep you on a knife-edge. Episodes are released sporadically – there's no set release date and your friends may receive the next episode before you do. All this uncertainty is going to make you nervous, which fulfils the aim of the app! If one of your favourite pastimes is bingeing on box sets from Netflix and LoveFilm, Haunting Melissa will either teach you some patience or drive you mad with anticipation.

From a functionality perspective, Haunting Melissa is extremely easy to use and keeps the buttons, icons and general clutter to a minimum. The app is controlled from a selection of five icons in the bottom left-hand corner of the app interface. Their functions range from Settings – where you can get help using the app or purchase a Season Pass – to Sharing, where you can get all of your friends involved with the Haunting Melissa adventure. When you're watching a chapter, the video control functions are virtually identical to those in the Movie app on your iPad or iPhone.

Despite the brilliant concept and innovative method of distribution, Haunting Melissa suffers from a serious lack of in-app interactivity. The extent of user interactivity is limited to connecting to external sites such as Facebook, Twitter, YouTube and the Haunting Melissa community – other than that, there's not much else to do other than sit and wait for the next

## "If you love bingeing on box sets, Haunting Melissa will either teach you some patience or drive you mad with anticipation"

■ The app's controls are really easy to use, letting you watch, rewind, share or pause

chapter to arrive. The app could really benefit from taking a 'choose your adventure' format, allowing the user to have an influence and make choices with regards to the direction the story takes, creating alternative narratives.

However, it should be noted that there is a lot to be gained from watching again. Each time you re-watch a chapter, certain details appear and disappear. In the first chapter for example, Melissa and her friend creep around the farmhouse in search of the source of an unsettling mewing sound coming from one of the rooms. As the camera pans around one of the rooms, a face can be briefly glimpsed in a shadow in the corner. But if you watch the chapter for a second time, the face has mysteriously vanished! It's enough for anyone to question their own vision and perception.

It would be perfectly acceptable to assume that a creepy, atmospheric series such as Haunting Melissa would be negatively affected by being scaled-down from a cinema size screen to the more modest screens of the iPad, iPhone and iPod. However, as the app is designed to immerse you into Melissa's world, it works brilliantly and

the sound has been designed to ramp up the spooky factor. If you prefer a larger screen though, Haunting Melissa supports AirPlay for Apple TV; simply tap the icon in each chapter to activate this and watch it on your TV-screen.

Whether you'll enjoy the story of Haunting Melissa is down to your own tastes. If even the most terrifying of horror movies have no effect on you, then you'll probably find this story a little tame, and you might get a bit bored. However, if the mere mention of ghosts and ghouls brings you out in a sweat, tuck yourself in a dark corner and cover your eyes.

**A great concept that creates tension but could be improved by letting users choose their story.**

★★★☆☆

■ More chapters are available through in-app purchases

**01: Start watching**
Tap on Chapter 1 in the top right-hand corner of the app's interface. Sit back, relax and simply watch the first instalment in its entirety.

**02: Unlock**
Once you've finished watching the chapter, a dialog box will appear asking you if you want to unlock Chapter 2 for free through sharing. Go ahead, you know you want to…

**03: Type a message**
Tap the Share on Facebook button. A Facebook Sharing prompt box will appear. Type a short message about the app using the keyboard.

**04: Share**
Once you've finished typing your message, tap the Post button. If you'd prefer not to post your message right now, simply tap the Cancel button and return to it later.

**05: Confirm**
A dialog box will confirm that you've successfully shared the app with your friends via Facebook. You'll receive a notification once the next chapter is available for download.

# Lifestyle

## Organise your time and get more done with your iPad

"The iPad can prove invaluable in helping you to work smarter"

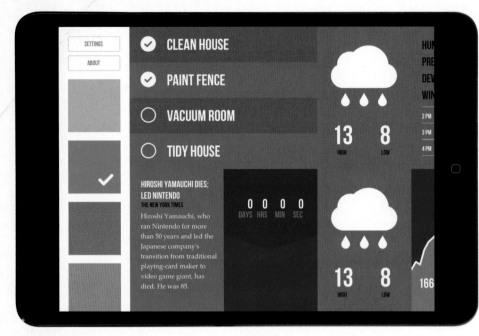

● Price £1.49/$2.99

■ In order to get started you must enable the weather, reminders and events features

■ Auto-location tailors the app to your specific locality so that you get the right information

# Morning – Weather, To-Do, News and more

## Shake off that bleary feeling with a morning data blast

### PROS/CONS

▲ A clean, effective and easy-to-read interface

▲ It taps into your ot her apps and location for spot-on service

▼ More panels are needed to create a true one-stop app

▼ SIt could use some more flexibility in its design

If you are anything like us, then you will likely wake up early each morning, grab a cup of tea or coffee and start to play around with your iPad in order to get your day going.

The Morning app caters for this very use, delivering a wealth of information on a single, well-designed screen so that you can see all the vital details that will get you on your way at a glance.

When you load the app for the first time you will see that it has a large clock with the date in the top-left of the screen, as well as blocks for weather and events. These need to be connected to your location and

to your calendar, with the reminders block needing to be synced with your Reminders app.

When you have done this, you begin to see the app's use. Suddenly you can view any specific tasks that you need to do that day, view the weather forecast and get a flavour of where you are expected to be without having to flick from one app to another.

Morning, however, goes even further than that. Although the interface is a relatively simple one, it actually masks a complex series of tasks that can be performed. For a start, you can change and customise all the blocks on the screen; so you could

decide not to have the weather in the top left-hand corner, for example, and place it elsewhere or even drop it entirely. You can also add in any extra functions with a host of panels available for you to tailor the page in the way that truly suits you.

For example, by tapping each box and selecting the icon to the left, you can choose one of eight different panels. These include Commute which lets you know what to expect on the roads when you leave the house, News allows you to pull in various different RSS sources, Stocks is there for keeping a close eye on the stock market and Countdown so that you know how long you have left before any important events starts.

By selecting these, the panel you have tapped will alter, changing the dynamic of the page and bringing in the information that you want to see and use. You can have these in any order you wish, and make the page suit your requirements. For example,

## "Although the interface is a relatively simple one, it actually masks a complex series of tasks that can be performed"

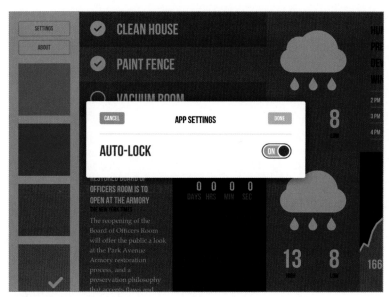

■ The app can be set to auto-lock if you so wish

having the weather app in a larger panel allows you see the humidity, wind and changing times of the day, whereas having it in a smaller one will simply show you the current weather and the highs and lows of the day. It means you can prioritise the information to a greater degree.

There is another icon when you press the panel too. The one to the left allows you to alter the settings of each window, so again, you can have more bespoke and personalised services. Perhaps you want your weather in Celsius rather than Fahrenheit (a thoughtful option), or you want your calendar to only display a specific event from birthdays to home to shopping, or even lectures and leisure activities.

Unfortunately, it's not all perfect. You can't add in your own extra panels, for example, so for now you're stuck with the predetermined sizes.

Additionally, while you can alter the colour of the screen, you can't tell the app to colour individual panels, which would be a handy feature. That said, this uniformity does make for a more sleek, less fussy and complex design that works well, so perhaps we are just being picky. Alarm clocks and

alert systems would be nice addition, though, and it would be good if you were able to input the countdown using scrolling menus rather than having to write it using text. More of an issue is not always being able to pull in the news feeds wanted and having to scroll down or wait to see each one, rather than simply being able to display the headlines at a glance.

Yet, we found ourselves always coming back to the app. We used it day after day, making it our first port of call. It cut down on the time spent jumping from one app to another which, when getting ready for work, can be quite annoying and potentially time-consuming.

To that end, Morning is a fine example of a one-stop shop information app. It needs more panels; eight is a good start but there are others that would come in useful – social media, for example). Still, for the price, it's well worth investing given the time it will save.

**Morning gets you up to date as soon as you wake, and it's a great sidekick throughout your day.**

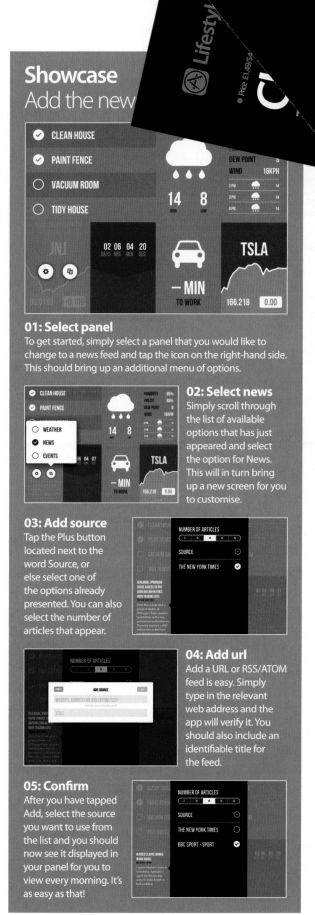

# Showcase
## Add the new

### 01: Select panel
To get started, simply select a panel that you would like to change to a news feed and tap the icon on the right-hand side. This should bring up an additional menu of options.

### 02: Select news
Simply scroll through the list of available options that has just appeared and select the option for News. This will in turn bring up a new screen for you to customise.

### 03: Add source
Tap the Plus button located next to the word Source, or else select one of the options already presented. You can also select the number of articles that appear.

### 04: Add url
Add a URL or RSS/ATOM feed is easy. Simply type in the relevant web address and the app will verify it. You should also include an identifiable title for the feed.

### 05: Confirm
After you have tapped Add, select the source you want to use from the list and you should now see it displayed in your panel for you to view every morning. It's as easy as that!

# Clear+

## The minimalist to-do list comes to iPad

When other mobile to-do lists had calendars, geo-location reminders, and a mass of on-screen buttons, the original Clear for iPhone bucked the trend. Instead, it just offered a single screen with items listed from urgent red to low priority yellow, with the option to swipe right to tick items when completed and drag down to add a new item to the list. This sequel makes the personal organiser with innovative one-touch controls available on iPad at last.

It's a mistake to expect too many new features from this famously minimalist app, but there are a few changes worth noting. Making the most of the extra space, all of your lists are displayed on the left-hand side, while the individual items fill the right.

As well as simplifying list browsing, this makes it easy to drag items between them.

However, not all of the new features come across as an improvement. The 'edge swipe' gesture to access the Settings doesn't feel as organic as swiping left to remove an item, like striking through with a pencil, and can be easily forgotten. If you access Settings, you can adapt the gestures

and change the colour theming. Making the most of iOS's Background Refresh function, the app also ensures that your iCloud backup stays updated.

**While it's a middle-of-the-road move for such an innovative brand, Clear+ is a comprehensive adaptation for iPad.**

★★★★★

---

● Price £2.49/$9.99

# Gneo

## A minimalist to-do manager that keeps on surprising

To-do apps are perhaps the most common of all productivity apps available today, but Gneo attempts to take a different view on how you should keep yourself organised by bringing your tasks and calendars together in one application. The ultra-minimalist interface may appear to be too simple for some, but it focuses the eye on the tasks more than any other app we have seen – plus the healthy balance between gestures and taps works very nicely. It feels natural from the first use and if you take the time to understand exactly how it works, you may become more organised than before in short order.

Gneo actually looks like a calendar in some views, which is a positive when it comes to overviewing what you need to get done. The priority view also places your tasks into

logical sections, which works particularly well on the iPad's larger screen. If you are also an Evernote user, the integration here could bring all of your most important information together – with a full set of data from your calendars, tasks and Evernote it could easily replace other apps straight away.

There are some quirks in the way it works that may not suit everyone and the minimalism is very sharp, perhaps taking away the visual enjoyment. Still, for its power and flexibility, Gneo offers users plenty of innovative benefits.

**A clever and clean way to bring your tasks, calendars and notes together under one smooth interface.**

★★★★☆

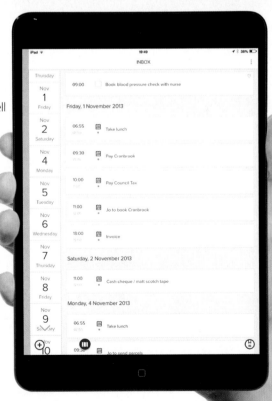

■ Gneo's layout is clear and organised, combining tasks and calendars

■ Everything is explained well when using Parallels Access, including how to use the toolbar

■ To move around the screen, simply use tapping and scrolling gestures

● Price Free

# Parallels Access

## Access your Mac or PC apps as if they were made for iPad

### PROS/CONS

▲ Control a computer via the iPad

▲ Use iPad-style controls, requiring little learning

▼ It costs £34.99/ $49.99 a year after a 14-day trial

▼ There is no dual use facility so the computer can't be used by anyone

 Parallels Access is a nifty little app that allows access to the desktop of a Mac or PC via an iPad. Users can control any Mac or PC program they open and use it as if it is running natively on the iPad. All that's needed is this app and some software installed on the computer and, with the two synced, it's all good to go.

Setting up is actually very easy, more so than users might typically expect from this type of app. Once the Mac had the right software installed, it was instantly picked up by the iPad and the two began working side by side. The Mac's Launchpad could then be opened for users to pick programs are wanted for use on the iPad. After that, users can tap away on icons and options, using two fingers for a right-click, and effectively operating the programs in the way users might expect if sat at a desk with a mouse.

The computer's desktop is replicated perfectly on the iPad in fullscreen mode. It is possible to zoom in and highlight words as well as cut, paste and open toolbars. The app is made so that users can utilise apps such as Microsoft Office, Internet Explorer and Photoshop and, when using a PC as well as a Mac, these all worked liked a dream.

■ Here we have the Mac's version of Pages running on the iPad

The main limitation is the fact that using Parallels Access puts the computer out of action while synced with the iPad – but there are lots of positives. These range from the ability to switch apps and windows with a tap or two and simple, iOS-style scrolling. It means the app has a nice learning curve since everything feels as if you are using your Apple device rather than trying to access a computer's functions on a smaller screen.

**An amazing and useful app that will enable users to have their computer on them at all times and caters to the busybody's every need.**

★★★★☆

## "The computer's desktop is replicated perfectly on the iPad in fullscreen mode"

● Price £6.99/$9.99

# Status Board

## Take your all-important data and display it beautifully

Convincing iPad owners that they need an app that displays their tweets, RSS feeds, calendars, emails and other vital statistics all in one place isn't easy. Set aside the issues surrounding data protection and you're left with a concept that sounds a little overwhelming and wholly unnecessary. Fortunately, Panic's Status Board waylays those concerns and provides users with a beautiful way to visualise the vital statistics that help you be more productive.

Status Board itself is based around a number of customisable panels that can be added, edited and resized in just a few taps. There's plenty of stock options to choose from, covering everything from the local weather to unread messages. The process for setting up the app and editing those panels is slick and seamless,

owing to a novel setup process that playfully nods to those infamous TV setup guides that made setting up your television such a chore. With setup out of the way, changing up the panels on your status board couldn't be easier, simply tap the Cog icon and tap and drag.

Despite its ease of use, this app doesn't lack power features. Status Board allows you to input HTML/JSON data to be visualised, even going as far as giving you the option to import your own HTML-based panels. In short, there's something here for everyone, but the issue is whether everyone will want it.

Status Board is the best data visualisation app we've seen. Rather than over-complicating, it keeps information clear and occasionally beautifully illustrated. The only problem it has is that not everyone will see the benefit beyond business and seriously great data geekery.

## "The process for setting up the app and editing the panels is slick and seamless"

**Whether you're a business or just love data visualisation, this app should definitely be on your iPad.**

★★★★☆

■ The app is a stellar example of how data visualisation can be functional as well as beautiful

■ Your Status Board is made up of a number of easily customised panels

■ The dock UI stores unused and new panels in the editing mode

■ The app's screen is divided between a day ticker or week view

■ The interface for Fantastical 2 is a breath of fresh air compared to the Calendar introduced in iOS7

▶ Price £5.49/$9.99

# Fantastical 2 for iPad

## Can the premier iPhone calendar app adapt to the iPad?

### PROS/CONS

▲ Better than Apple's native app

▲ Offers natural-language input

▼ Day ticker is a bit pointless in reality

▼ Some minor reminders grumbles

Apple's iOS 7 Calendar overhaul for iPad didn't go down terribly well. Through religiously adhering to Jony Ive's penchant for minimal interfaces, the result is a fiddly app that somehow manages to be both cluttered and waste space. Fortunately, Fantastical has now made its way over to larger Apple devices. And this news makes us happy, because it's very, very good indeed.

Fantastical 2 packs everything onto a single screen rather than using tabs. Across the top there's a day ticker, providing an overview of the current week, with little lozenges representing appointments. Below, a scrolling list details upcoming events, omitting empty days for efficiency; alongside is a basic month view. The ticker's fairly pointless in the iPhone version, but on the iPad it can be switched for a more useful week view. In portrait, it's a pity the amount of space the week view takes up can't be fine-tuned, but Fantastical largely manages to do on one screen what Apple's app fails to do in three.

The app's crowning glory, though, remains its natural-language input. As you add an event, using plain-English, it builds before your eyes, enabling you to make adjustments as you go. It's intuitive, effective, efficient

and surprisingly fun. As a nice touch, add a meal and the app automatically assigns the event to an appropriate time. Again as per the iPhone version, this iPad release retains the original's slew of options and a workable, if slightly feature-light and tacked-on means of dealing with reminders. The lack of sort options for reminders is a pity, but as Fantastical uses standard iCloud information, it means you can avoid one of Apple's worst iOS apps!

**Despite some minor misgivings, by far the best iPad calendar app, obliterating Apple's own. A quick, simple way to get organised.**

★★★★★

"It manages to do on one screen what Apple's app fails to do in three"

■ Unlike on iPhone, week view doesn't require flipping your device

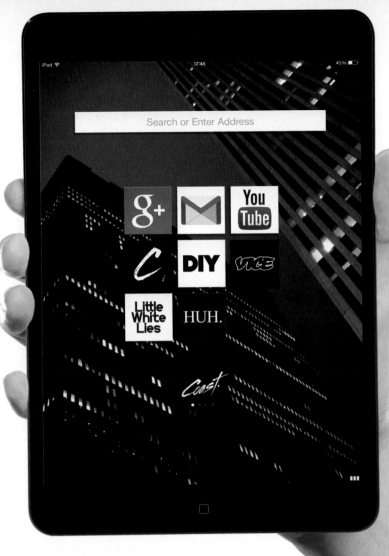

■ The search bar attempts to auto-complete your searches

■ Multitask with ease using the swipe-able browser tabs

● Price Free

# Coast by Opera

## Manage your webpages like app icons in this iPad-only browser

### PROS/CONS

▲ Webpages fill almost the entire screen

▲ Gesture controls make it easy to navigate

▼ No control over privacy or web history

▼ The city-by-night background looks a little dated

 The web has evolved exponentially from drab, grey webpages to vivid, elegant pages with complex graphics, videos and other interactive information. Yet, so far, the web experience on tablets has been limited to browsers that are either scaled-up versions of smartphone browsers or scaled-down desktop browsers. Web developers Opera wanted to fix this. Enter Coast, a browser specifically designed for surfing on your iPad.

During the year and a half it took to develop, the app was codenamed Ice, but Coast – as in 'coasting along' – suits its relaxed, easy-to-use nature better. Not that the browser is slow. When we carried out speed tests on loading times, Coast was faster than both Google's Chrome and Dolphin. The only browsers we could find that benchmarked better were Safari and

Puffin. Safari's speed is no surprise; Apple ensures it runs faster on iOS by giving it its own dedicated server and forcing all third-party apps to share one. Puffin, however, compresses webpages before it downloads them, so it was three times faster even than Safari. But Puffin's drab design doesn't compare to Coast's stylish interface.

Rather than waste screen space with buttons, Coast makes the most of your touchscreen and boasts an impressive number of features that are entirely gesture controlled. Do you want to move backwards and forwards between webpages? Just swipe left and right. Want to close a tab or delete

a favourite page from the main menu? Just drag it to the top of the screen where a yawning black void will appear to swallow it up. If you tap the tiny button that is permanently at the bottom of the screen, you can view screenshots of every open page in a carousel – like your new iOS 7 iPad's multitasking feature. Similar to multasking, you can swipe upwards to close pages, but if you swipe down Coast runs a quick security check on how safe the webpage is.

The white bar at the top of the screen we also found to be highly intuitive. As a universal search field you can enter either full web addresses or just keywords to search for, and it will auto-suggest related words and websites so you don't have to even finish what you were typing.

## "This functional way to navigate and interact with the web could change the way you browse the Internet and use apps on the iPad"

Coast goes even further by providing preview pictures of webpages, which is particularly helpful for when you're trying to locate a specific website, but can't remember its name.

However, though Coast's PR team has been eager to claim it's a 'buttonless' browser, this isn't strictly true. In an effort to create a tablet-friendly way to surf the web, Opera seems to have taken inspiration from how Apple put together the iPad. Just as the iPad displays its various programs as tappable app icons, Coast does the same for webpages. While this might sound cluttered, it makes for a tidy mosaic of coloured squares, with your favourite webpages grouped in the centre of the screen and open pages scrolling across the bottom.

Don't mistake this feature for just a novel style choice though, as this functional way to navigate and interact with the web could change the way you browse the Internet and use apps on your iPad. Coast offers an innovative way to bookmark your favourite sites, making apps that exist only as a portal for websites, such as Facebook, Buzzfeed or Google Drive, obsolete.

This is reflected by the websites that are preloaded onto Coast's main menu, which include Pinterest, Soundcloud and Gmail as well as magazine

websites including Vice and the British Journal of Photography. With all of these popular features easily accessible within Coast, you're encouraged to stay within this single app. Has this browser imitated the iPad's home screen and gesture controls so thoroughly that it might become your new home screen? It's certainly possible.

Where the app does fall down is in its lack of control over privacy; unlike with other browsers, there is no option to switch to private browsing. On top of that, if you want to delete your web history you have to do it in the iPad's own settings. This seems a particularly backwards move for an app that otherwise encourages you to stay within its interface.

The app's monochrome city-by-night backdrop and seemingly handwritten logo arguably seem a little dated. However, you rarely actually see this branding except for when you're navigating to another webpage.

Still, these are only minor complaints that shouldn't put you off at least trying out this innovative new app – you may find that its features suit you perfectly.

**An elegant browser that could change how you browse and make you delete a variety of apps.**

■ Websites take up the whole screen with no distracting buttons

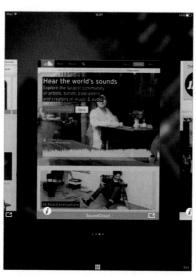

## Showcase
## Navigate with a single swipe

### 01: Tap to search
Tap the white bar at the top of the screen to type and start your search for web addresses and key phrases. Open a few windows to see how easy it is to navigate.

### 02: Back and forth
Rather than pressing arrow buttons, simply swipe left and right to seamlessly move backwards and forwards between your open webpages.

### 03: Main menu
To exit from any window, all you have to do is tap the small white mosaic button at the bottom of the screen to return to the main menu and your bookmarks.

### 04: Close pages
To actually shut down active pages, first tap the button in the bottom-right to view a carousel of all open tabs. Swiping them upwards will close the tabs immediately.

### 05: Safety first
Swipe down in this screen for a safety report of to how much the webpages are trusted. Double tapping this screen will give you extra information.

● Price Free

# Duolingo

 Amazingly, this language-learning system is completely free. You can use it to learn six languages: Spanish, French, German, Portuguese, Italian and English. Courses start with some basic vocabulary, before progressing to more advanced speech and reading exercises. A brilliant app.

**An excellent tool that offers a huge amount and is still free.**

★★★★★

● Price £4.99/$6.99

# Calendars 5

 Calendars 5 integrates perfectly with both Google Calendar and iOS Calendar and allows for list, week or month formats. It comes with some great features like pinpointing meetings with Maps, making use of your Contacts, and specifying the exact frequency of events.

**A first-class app that uses real language for inputting. Brilliant.**

★★★★★

● Price £0.69/$0.99

# My Recipe Book

 While the ace Android app ChefTap isn't yet available on iOS, this is a credible alternative. The digital equivalent of taking cuttings from magazines, it lets you import recipes. You can also input your own and add photos. They can then be viewed offline, shared with friends or synced with other devices.

**The digital replacement for recipe cards in a box, and a decent alternative.**

★★★★★

● Price £1.99/$2.99

# AirPano Travel Book

 The AirPano Travel Book is great as it takes you around the world and lets you explore them in the most immersive of ways. The panoramas are genuine 360° aerial shots, making it feel as if you are flying over each location. Addictive.

**A breathtaking app that amazes and surprises.**

★★★★★

● Price £2.99/$4.99

# Pinswift

 Pinboard is a hugely successful bookmarking service, but the quality of available mobile apps has never reached the standard it deserves. In Pinswift, however, we have an app that cleanly presents all of your bookmarks in an interface which feels modern and which highlights the content perfectly. It is reliable, the built-in browser works perfectly.

**One of the best Pinboard clients we have seen.**

★★★★★

● Price £0.69/$0.99

# Wymfo

 When you have connected Wymfo to your cloud services and added the contacts you deal with the most often, you may wonder why no one has thought of this before. Wymfo allows you to share content held in any of your cloud services with anyone by simply dragging and dropping files. So incredibly simple!

**A simple yet stunning cloud sharing solution that works on every level.**

★★★★★

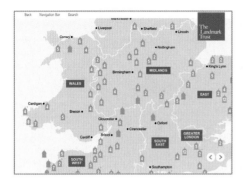

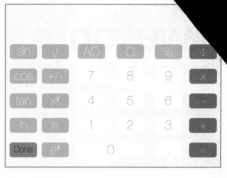

● Price £0.69/$4.99

● Price £2.99/$4.99

● Price £0.69/$0.99

# Landmark Trust

There is no doubting the quality of the presentation and the efficient way this app details all of the available Landmark Trust locations. It almost feels like a high-quality magazine, but as this is a promotional app, the price is a concern.

**A professional way to sell a service, but the price is a little high for most.**

★★★☆☆

# Zumba Dance

The Zumba app simulates one-on-one instructional fitness programs, and feels like a professional fitness video, but allows you to customise it to your specific needs. You can monitor your progress and use the tutorial mode to practise. It's a great example of how to bring professional fitness to mobile devices.

**Offers the chance to carry fun fitness with you everywhere.**

★★★★★

# OfficeDesk

OfficeDesk is designed to give you a planner, notepad, calculator and a voice recorder all under one virtual roof. If you spend a lot of time at your desk with your iPad close to you, this system actually works more efficiently than you may expect, and over time starts to get under your skin and demand your attention.

**A great integration of often-used apps into a system that will save you time.**

★★★★☆

● Price £0.69/$0.99

● Price £1.49/$1.99

● Price £1.99/$2.99

# SecretLondon

Perhaps more useful for those visiting London rather than its residents, Secret London provides hidden gems to explore in the capital. These are shown by icons on a map, for categories such as activities, food, drinks, shops, museums and oddities. Tap on one to reveal a photo and detailed info, plus sharing options.

**Best for those new to London, this is a useful app for finding exciting places.**

★★★★☆

# Write for iPad

Write for iPad is full of advanced features, but somehow hides all of this complexity in an app that feels destined for the iPad. The keyboard includes a magic cursor for fast navigating, plus rich markdown editing support. Add to this seamless synchronisation, image support and a calm interface.

**Complexity meets simple elegance in this winning writing app.**

★★★★★

# Clean and Green Eating

Few health apps concentrate on tasty offerings and present them as professionally as Clean and Green Eating. The number of recipes is not huge, but they are impressive, and if you need ideas this is a good place to start. Perfect for anyone wanting to eat healthily.

**A professional and interesting way to obtain new recipes and to eat healthily.**

★★★★★

# ne Note for iPad

## ecision with this all-in-one tool

Awesome Note for iPad calls itself the most innovative all-in-one life organiser, and, when you look at the amount it manages to pack in, you can understand why. For a start, its interface is smart and appealing. It takes your wallpaper as its backdrop, dividing the screen up well with a list of the day's tasks running down the right-hand side in a tidy window. A calendar and other useful functions are located at the top and to the left of the screen and there are a series of very colourful folders.

When you open up the app, you will notice that some of these folders will already have some entries from the developers. This is a little frustrating, but they can easily be deleted. Each of the folders can be customised to suit your needs: you can assign them a name, icon and colour scheme and also choose the default settings for each one, saving you time and hassle. The format for each folder is largely the same; there's a calendar displaying the current month and beneath it any tasks assigned for a particular highlighted day. They can be sorted by the date modified or created, or by name, due date and priority, all of which makes searching easier.

It only takes around ten minutes or so for you to get to grips with the app. You can sync with your existing Calendar and Reminders and manage them as a folder. The app also works with Google Drive and Evernote, which makes it a great integrated app.

With an app like this we're aware of the need for protection, and thankfully it has a passcode function. The app did crash once when we tried to attach some photos to a note. Still, in every other respect it appears to be robust, which is important when it's to be used every day.

---

**Awesome Note cuts out the need for organisational app hopping and proves to be impossible to live without once you get going.**

★★★★★

## "Tasks can be sorted by date, name, due date and priority, all of which makes searching easier"

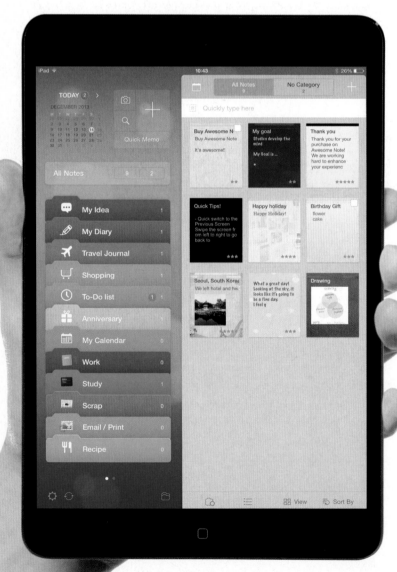

■ A passcode can be set for the app to stop any prying eyes seeing your information

■ There are many ways you can alter the way the app works in the Settings menu

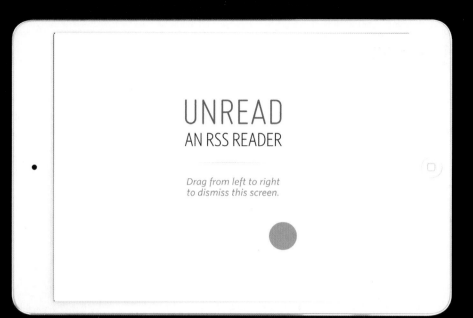

Grillography: Here's Your BBQ-Inspired Typeface!

NEATORAMA
*Alex Santoso*
*15 Jun 2014 21:00*

Summer is almost here (though from the hot, hot weather, it feels that it's already been here a while), so you know what this means, Neatoramanauts: it's BBQ time!

◼ Whatever the source website happens to be, articles are presented in a clean and clear layout

◼ Unread aims to put the focus back on the content with a strikingly minimal approach

● Price £2.99/$4.99

# Unread for iPad
## Elegant, minimal RSS reader

### PROS/CONS

▲ Clean and attractive interface with several themes.

▲ Intuitive, natural, straightforward way of navigating feeds.

▼ Setup is quick, but an existing RSS client is required.

▼ Limited number of customisation options available

For the uninitiated, you can think of RSS (Really Simple Syndication) as an older, slower and more involved version of Twitter, enabling users to keep tabs on multiple sites through one app. Unread isn't an RSS reader, but it plugs into your existing service — Feedly, FeedWrangler, Feedbin, Fever and NewsBlur are supported — to offer a beautifully minimal way of reading through online content.

From the simple swipe-based interface method to the well-chosen fonts and colours, this is an app that exudes quality. Setup is straightforward, the options are clear and the integrated sharing interface enables you to tell your friends about something you've come across online with a couple of taps. In the words of its developer, Unread is designed to help you "rediscover the joy of reading", and that's a good way of thinking about how the app works.

It's really your RSS client of choice that's doing the hard work — Unread focuses on presenting the content in a more appealing way. It makes a difference with the full-screen reading mode, carefully crafted interface and intuitive controls all adding up to a worthwhile app.

The articles you've signed up to read take centre-stage. Unread brings more pleasure to the process of catching up with whatever you're following on the internet. It doesn't offer as many features as something like Reeder, but that stripped-down approach works really well here. Starring articles, marking them as read or moving on to the next story can all be done with a flick of a finger, and if you're an RSS addict you'll find Unread incredibly useful.

**An attractively designed and intuitive RSS tool that puts the focus on reading. Ideal if you don't want to miss out on your favourite content.**

★★★★★

> "Unread brings more pleasure to the process of catching up with whatever you're following online"

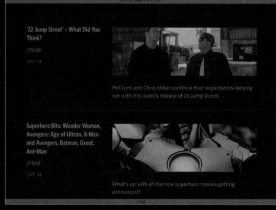

◼ The app sticks to a one-column interface to reduce clutter

● Price £1.99/$2.99

# The Whole Pantry

## A selection of recipes, guides and books for health and wellness

 Eating well and exercising frequently are inextricably linked to living healthily – and The Whole Pantry offers advice on both. Packed with glorious food photography, users can select from 37 recipes including drinks, mains, salads, snacks and even condiments.

Presented as a mosaic gallery of photos, a single tap rotates images to list recipe names and whether they are gluten free, dairy free and suitable for vegetarians. A double tap loads a fullscreen gallery of one or more images. Swipe upwards to view a summary of the dish, ingredients list and step-by-step instructions.

The Guides section offers leisurely reads that you can dip in and out of easily. It features, for instance, lists of the top ten super foods and a nice introduction to yoga for beginners.

The Our Pantry section is also packed with lists of recommended cookbooks, documentaries, TV shows and products for healthy food and living. However, with external links only to blogs and websites and no other explanatory descriptions, this particular section seemed a little bare.

Other features include a search engine to filter by ingredients, a Favourites window, and the option to share recipes and guides. The information that's here is well-presented and useful for expectant parents, though there's a big disclaimer shown as you launch the app for the first time: you should be using it alongside advice from your doctor, not instead of. Extras such as a weight tracker,

■ The Pantry section includes lists of books, films, websites and products promoting food and healthy living put together

a kick counter, a contraction timer and a doctor's appointment book all add to the appeal of the app, and £1.99 isn't much to part with considering the wealth of material you get.

**The emphasis on holistic medicine will be a Marmite issue, but all foodies will love the image-driven recipes.**

★★★★☆

---

● Price £2.99/$4.99

# TimeQuote

## Get straight to the interesting moments of any recording

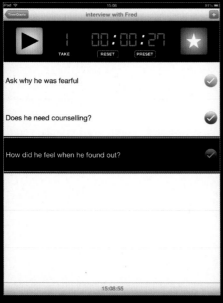

■ Pre-script interviews and include key questions and prompts before shooting

 Created for journalists and videographers, Timequote has been produced by former ITN reporter James Woodman. It enables professionals to log key quotes and to chart important moments during an interview. Journalists can jump to important parts of a recording without searching, or relying on notes.

It's a rather simple creation with large bold times displayed at the top, a Play/Stop button and a star. When recording begins, you need to tap Play on the iPad at the same time. Then, when you hear or notice something that you want to include in a subsequent edit, you tap the star button to mark it. Tapping on the '+' button goes even further and enables you to make notes, whether they be descriptive of the moment

or something to discuss later on. But the '+' button has an even better use. By adding in questions and prompts before you start interviewing, you can ensure that you ask everything you need. When you get to that point in the filming, tapping on the question will mark it on the timeline so you know the precise moment it was asked and can go to it during editing.

It has bags of potential. For the price, we'd love for it to include audio-recording, and be available on smartphones too. That would make this brilliant tool even more portable and useful for professionals.

**An effective time-saving app for journalists and videographers covering interviews and press conferences.**

 ★★★★☆

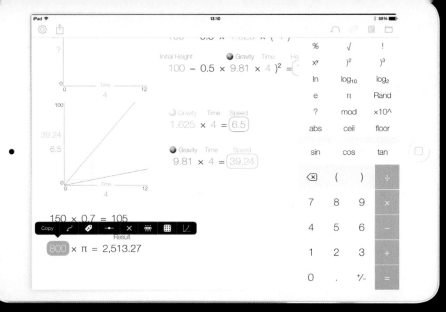

● Price £0.99/$4.99

# Tydlig

## Advanced calculator tool with an appealing layout

Tydlig boldly announces itself as 'the calculator reimagined'. Thankfully, it has the features to back up its claim: this slick app is packed with functionality. You can go back and edit calculations on the fly, link calculations together and even produce some impressive-looking graphs. Labelling tools enable you to put text or emot... your numbers and when your work... you can export as PDF or print it out. A... your previous calculations are saved, so you can scroll back up to revisit them.

If you find yourself trying to work out mortgage repayments, shop discounts or mileage on the back of an envelope, Tydlig is a hugely superior replacement. Its intelligent use of colours and free-form layout (similar to OneNote or Evernote) means that you can customise it to suit you. This flexibility occasionally led to problems — we would sometimes try and clear a calculation only to see a graph disappear instead — but this didn't happen often, and you'll quickly get used to it. There is a learning curve here, but it won't distract from Tydlig's benefits.

**A beautifully designed calculator with some useful little features – and all with a relatively small price tag.**

★★★★★

● Price £2.49

# One Born Every Minute: Pregnancy Day By Day

## A comprehensive guide to having a baby

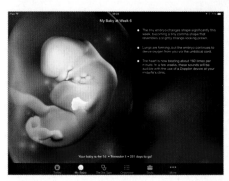

One Born Every Minute is a Channel 4 documentary on the journey through pregnancy, and this is the tie-in app — it sticks to providing information about your pregnancy though, and there are no episode clips or interviews on offer. What you do you get is a reasonably in-depth selection of resources you can use to chart the progress of your baby's growth: timelines and annotated images illustrate exactly what stage you're at, the conditions you should be looking out for and what you can expect in the future. There are reminders too for logging information about your pregnancy and setting up checkups. The information that's here is well-presented and useful for expectant parents, though there's a big disclaimer shown as you launch the app for the first time — you should be using it alongside advice from your doctor. Extras such as a weight tracker, a kick counter, a contraction timer and a doctor's appointment book (complete with a notes section for questions) all add to the appeal of the app, and £2.49 isn't much to part with considering the impressive functions and content that come with it. There's even a checklist for heading to the hospital when the time comes.

**Plenty of useful information for mums-to-be to pore over– and it's all elegantly presented as well.**

★★★★☆

■ The 3D visualisations are realistic and very nicely put together

# ...ocus

## ...en managing a group

...o lose sight ...or goals ... with lots of short-term tasks. LeaderFocus aims to help managers prioritise their work and manage time more productively so that longer term objectives are met.

Aside from the lurid orange colouring, the app is neat and comprehensive, working across numerous screens to cover four main areas: the focus for the day, strategic objectives, short-term tasks and delegated responsibilities. There is also a page for daily leadership thoughts in case you are lacking inspiration.

The app says it is not a to-do list, and we have to agree that it doesn't come across as one. All of the input boxes are short and intuitive so you don't get bogged down with processes. And although you can add

work tasks, stress their importance and note when they need to be done, they are then placed on the main page in three boxes marked Events, Focus and Deadlines, giving a simple at-a-glance view of the day ahead.

The app also positions tasks in boxes that are placed on the screen in order of urgency and importance. By going further than this and allowing you to set long-term objectives, highlight self-development goals and listing what you need to achieve your aims, LeaderFocus soon comes into its own.

**In concentrating on results we figure that this app will really boost your productivity level.**

★★★★★

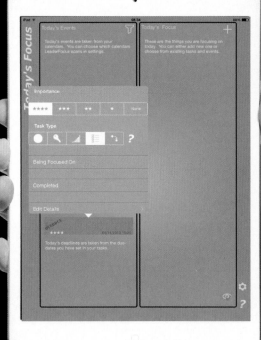

■ Tasks can be quickly edited and you can indicate when it is being focused on

● Price £2.49/$3.99

# The Photo Cookbook

## A simple and delicious collection for novices

■ The app provides plenty of images and information to help beginners get going

If variety is the spice of life, being able to mix it up at meal times couldn't fail to make every day that little bit more interesting. If you feel that you are unskilled in the kitchen, the prospect of learning how to sauté, grill, bake and broil could be enough to give you indigestion. Thankfully, The Photo Cookbook – Simple and Delicious is here.

The app aims to help newbies overcome their culinary concerns with a range of simple recipes grouped under Starters, Pastas and Pizzas, Main Dishes and Desserts. The main menu is a grid of tasteful images of meals that include basic classics such as fried ham and cheese sandwiches and spaghetti bolognese as well as more exotic fare such as mozzarella-stuffed chicken and a tasty mushroom stroganoff.

Tapping on an image brings up the recipe, beginning with a photo of the ingredients. Below are cooking steps consisting of short passages of text and pictures of what you should see at each stage. Nutritional information for each recipe is accessible from an icon at the top of screen, where you can also add notes, flag favourites and share recipes.

The number of recipes included with the app is limited but if you've been avoiding the oven, they should give you confidence to move on to more advanced titles once you've had your fill.

**The clear design and concise instructions should satisfy even the most demanding app-etite.**

★★★★★

■ The interface is minimal and yet well organised

■ Easily print your work directly from the app

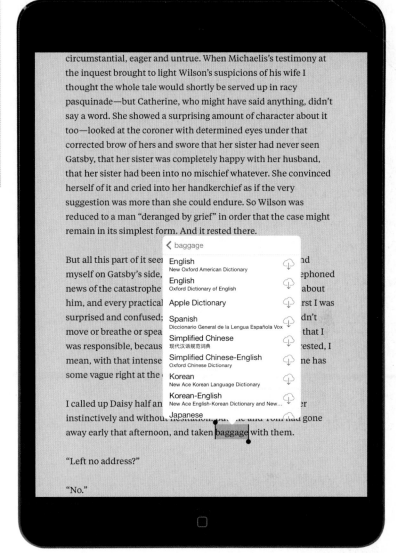

● Price £6.99/£4.99

# Writer Pro

## Improve your writing workflow and avoid being distracted

At around the time of the iPad's inception, an app arrived that caught the imagination of writers. Called iA Writer, it was, some would say, akin to the 'Emperor's New Clothes'.

In stripping away the various elements of distraction that tend to clutter a typical word processor (formatting buttons, sharing options and so on), iA Writer was a simple editor. It was making a feature out of lacking features, so to speak.

But it worked. We found ourselves focusing much more on the words rather than how they were presented on the screen. It became an iPad classic. So we look at Writer Pro with some skepticism. Pro? Doesn't that complicate things?

Actually, it doesn't. At the bottom of the main screen there are five options that help create a sense of workflow. You are able to view your most recent documents, make notes, write, edit and read. Functionally, each of these options is identical but you go through these stages and expand upon your work until it's in the final stage.

In some respects though, Writer Pro is not strictly without distraction. The keyboard has a fair amount on it besides the important Qwerty keys. You can use the iPad's microphone to dictate your words and call up a selection of Emojis. You can add punctuation, skip from word to word and swipe across to see character and word counts. Tapping the screen gives cut, copy and paste options and you can also define words. The app

then allows you to print, share your work across social networks or email and even open the text in another app entirely.

For the privilege, you do have to stump up some money. In a world where Pages is free on newer iDevices, the cost is rather high for what, dare we say, is a rather pretentious offering when all is said and done. Yet, it has proven to be useful. It's great that it syncs between other iOS devices and it's good to have the writing process laid bare and yet feel somewhat more organised. Still, you'll likely have to be a very keen writer to be willing to pay out for such a simple app.

**A good expansion on the original but remains expensive for what is; ultimately, a spin on a text editor. Nevertheless, it will work well for some.**

★★★☆☆

### PROS/CONS

▲ It does well at improving your writing workflow

▲ It is easy to use and lets you concentrate on the words

▼ It costs quite a lot for its level of complexity

▼ It's a departure from the original aim of a distraction-free writing tool

# 30 Day Green Smoothie

## This healthy offering serves up a challenge

The 30 Day Green Smoothie Challenge app is a simple one. It's about smoothies. Green ones.

The design is clean and simple and the pictures look vibrant and tasty (as the smoothies turn out to be in reality, as well). You can either dive straight into a 30-day programme, or select from the recipes.

The app is welcoming to novices; it offers guidance on shopping for ingredients, what goes together and what sort of blender you might like, all in plain, straightforward English. It also manages to avoid the health-crazy tone often associated with programmes of this ilk. There is even a guide on substitutions in case you're not a fan of a certain ingredient, so it's perfectly okay not to like kale. The challenge itself is also very simple to follow.

Press the button and a list of 30 smoothies pops up. You can add the ingredients for each smoothie onto a shopping list, which even divides the ingredients according to aisles, for us easily confused ones.

The challenge is strict, as you can't skip or switch a smoothie if you don't have the right ingredients that day, but the ready-made 5-day shopping list is designed to prevent that happening. This is a challenge, after all. The wide range of smoothies ensures variety if you want to re-take the challenge, although regrettably, there isn't a bacon smoothie. We checked.

**30 Day Green Smoothie is a simple download for anyone looking for a healthy detox.**

★★★★★

■ Not a fan of courgettes? No problem, you can discover a wide range of other flavours

---

● Price Free

# PerfectMind

## Chart your ideas with this basic mind-mapping tool

Mind mapping, brainstorming, doodling… whatever your preferred term for the practice happens to be, it is what PerfectMind does. It lets you link your ideas and thoughts together — whether it's a project for work or a recipe for the kitchen — and display them

easily on screen, plotting and rearranging them as required. You can export your maps in a variety of formats from the main menu (including PDF and PNG). The interface doesn't look too bad, but unfortunately the app doesn't have much else going for it. Not only are there plenty of other tools that do

the same job in the App Store, PerfectMind is light on really useful features (you can't change colours or shapes, for example, only pick from different themes) and unfortunately has one or two glaring errors (such as the iCloud Share option).

We experienced several unexplained crashes during use, as well. At least the interface is clean and straightforward, and the option to add icons to your bubbles is a nice touch. There is a slightly more advanced version available for Mac OS which you can pick up for £2.99/$4.99.

If you're planning a novel or building up a complex to-do list then PerfectMind will do at a pinch (and it is free, after all). But for more extensive purposes, we think that there are much better alternatives to be found out there, such as SimpleMind+.

---

**It does get the basic mind mapping tools right, but doesn't offer much beyond that.**

★★★☆☆

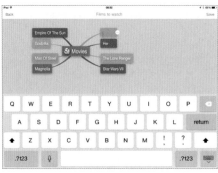

■ PerfectMind lets you choose from several colour themes for your mind maps

■ From movie lists to work projects, the app can adapt to different tasks

**Price** Free

# Google Sheets

Google has tried to decrease the work involved in creating spreadsheets on a mobile device with Google Sheets and overall has made a good effort. However, we found that the interface lent itself more to creating very simple sheets than the ones you are more likely to use, and feel that more features are needed to make it truly worthwhile. Sheets is suitable for casual calculation, but not sophisticated enough for professional use.

**A decent attempt at simplifying spreadsheet creation, but it's perhaps too simple to be really useful.**

★★★☆☆

**Price** £1.49/$1.99

# Calzy

Calzy is as minimalist as a calculator can get, but that should not divert your attention from its hidden clever features. The calculation history lets you perform multiple calculations without forgetting any and the spell out feature allows every day use. The splendid interface tops it off – this is your next default app.

**A brilliant alternative to the default offering with extra features.**

★★★★★

**Price** £0.69/$0.99

# My Notebook

This app's ability to deal with all types of media – including photos, sketches and recordings – is impressive, and it will enable you to keep all of the important information that you require together. The interface is clean and simple enough to let the data shine through and, best of all, there is also a very small learning curve. It would be nice, however, for the app to have a bit more of a professional finish to its design.

**A flexible note-taking app that is particularly well suited to the larger iPad screen.**

★★★☆☆

---

**Price** £2.99/$4.99

# DropTask HD

## Manage individual and team tasks with ease

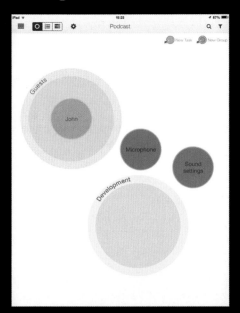

■ The simplistic, minimalist visual interface greatly

Creating complex task lists is a difficult enough undertaking when it's only you who needs to view and understand it – but to then explain what you are doing to a team of people is even harder. As projects evolve and the complexity increases, so does the confusion and lack of control.

DropTask HD - Visual To-Do List attempts to do away with all of that by using easy-to-understand visuals. You start by building groups, which can then be populated by adding individual tasks. This keeps everything neatly arranged and also ensures that separate parts of the project do not negatively impact others. Invites can be sent to enable real-time calibration and this is where the visual aspects really

instant and the entire team will understand why – and the various views will help you even more.

There is the option to view a traditional list or add more detail to each task, but what remains is always simple to view and quick to drill down within. Most projects, and even individual task lists, benefit from simplification; DropTask HD manages this and offers its users the chance to complete a complex project much quicker, and with fewer mistakes and misscommunications. Collaboratively it is highly effective, but it has many uses outside of that.

**A highly effective collaborative project solution that simplifies the entire process in style.**

★★★★★

● Price £0.69/$0.99

# Claire

## Focus on the most urgent tasks with this iPad-exclusive download

Claire is not the most descriptive of names for an app. What you see from the icon and what you decipher from the name and what you end up getting will not, we suggest, immediately go hand-in-hand. At first glance, it could have been a female play on the electronic game Simon – which it it's not. What it is, however, is something very useful aiming to change the way you work.

Claire is an organisational tool that hopes to revolutionise the way you deal with your time. Before you get on and start to tinker with the app, it explains this in great detail. First there is 300 word document that attempts to explain the importance of making time for the things you want to do and why it is crucial to recognise when something isn't worth doing. Second, there are diagrams that hammer home that point. Only by reading these do you get a real sense of what is going and why you are doing it.

The main screen of the app is split into four blocks, each one colour co-ordinated. It works on the Pareto principle that 20 per cent of our tasks cause 80 per cent of the effects and vice versa. The blocks represent, clockwise from left, your schedule, the items you need to do urgently, the items that can be delegated or ignored and those that can be binned. This, it says, is the Eisenhower principle.

Within each of these squares, which are coloured orange, red, yellow and grey, are a series of tasks. The app starts with suggestions to give you a good idea of what needs to go where but you are supposed to erase these and insert your own. What you put in these is entirely up

to you. You could schedule time for sport and relaxation, or make sure you get time for a report or essay that may need doing in a couple of weeks, and so on.

You could place a crisis meeting or a letter from the taxman in urgent. You could also place any tasks that you could feasibly get someone else to do – such as the gardening or a phone call – in the delegation list or simply forget about it. Everything else you can trash.

Writing new entries is an easy process. Depending on the category into which you are assigning tasks, you can set a date and a reminder. You can also move items from one category to another just by tapping on it and selecting the colour of the block you want to move it

### PROS/CONS

▲ You can place tasks in one of four categories

▲ The design feels very intuitive

▼ You can't write a full description of the task at hand

▼ Why would you list items in trash in the first place?

■ This is perhaps the most crucial explanation showing you the significance of the blocks

■ Is such urgency really necessary?' Questioning yourself motivates you to be organised

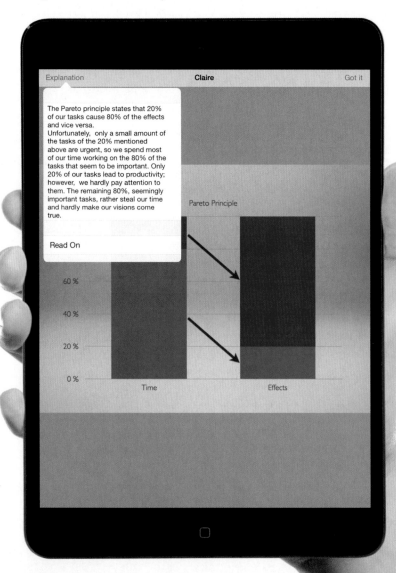

■ The app offers various tips for helping you manage your task list more effectively

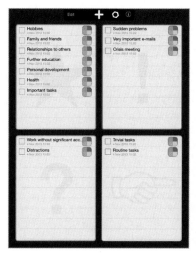

■ All of the tasks you input in Claire are placed on the same screen for easy viewing

to. Items within each block can be moved up or down so you can set their priority, and you can also bring in items from your Reminders app so you can get started without having to re-input everything.

Tasks can be assigned time slots and by default this is 30 minutes. You can also set automatic alerts and, for tidiness, have the app delete any task that has been completed. But this is secondary to the fundamental principle that not all tasks are of equal importance and that a productive use of the day is not to go through items on your desk one-by-one, maybe getting the smaller and easier items done first and then tackling the more difficult and time-consuming later. It drills in that a task may not be important at all and that you may be better served going out to play that game of squash instead.

Claire works well and is incredibly refreshing. The design is superbly clear with large icons and a clean look. The tips whenever you are

about to insert an entry are helpful, and this means at no point does Claire let you forget what you are doing, which is managing your time. It doesn't let you think you are merely creating lists and it prompts you to think carefully about where you want to put an item before you create it.

By making Claire a simple app to understand and use, it also adheres the principle of not wasting unnecessary time. The four blocks of tasks, each displayed on the same screen, is what makes this so effective because you can mark things up, tick them off and move them around as your priorities change without tapping back and forth between lists. You know straight away what you have to do and what you don't – what more could you ask for?

**An inexpensive task manager that doesn't completely leave you alone and makes sure you prioritise well.**

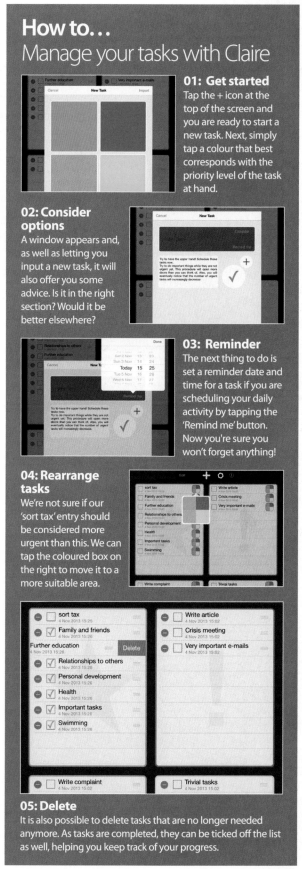

# How to...
## Manage your tasks with Claire

**01: Get started**
Tap the + icon at the top of the screen and you are ready to start a new task. Next, simply tap a colour that best corresponds with the priority level of the task at hand.

**02: Consider options**
A window appears and, as well as letting you input a new task, it will also offer you some advice. Is it in the right section? Would it be better elsewhere?

**03: Reminder**
The next thing to do is set a reminder date and time for a task if you are scheduling your daily activity by tapping the 'Remind me' button. Now you're sure you won't forget anything!

**04: Rearrange tasks**
We're not sure if our 'sort tax' entry should be considered more urgent than this. We can tap the coloured box on the right to move it to a more suitable area.

**05: Delete**
It is also possible to delete tasks that are no longer needed anymore. As tasks are completed, they can be ticked off the list as well, helping you keep track of your progress.

# "By making Claire a simple app to understand and use, it also adheres the principle of not wasting time"

# Education & Kids

## Apps to keep young ones entertained while they learn

Pick and grow your own vegetables.

"You can only spend so much time on your device before the children become curious about the source of entertainment"

• Price £3.99/$5.99

■ The story moves through all four weather seasons, so there is a great range of colour on show

■ The character are recognisable and engaging, and make for some great digital friends

# Lucy Ladybird

## A charming tale to delight the younger generation

### PROS/CONS

▲ The artwork looks fantastic on the iPad screen

▲ Colouring In and Karaoke sections are fun extras

▼ On-screen interactivity could perhaps be bigger and better

▼ The story might be too simple for older children

There is only so long an iPad user can sit, playing on their device before their children become curious about the source of entertainment and want to get involved themselves. Luckily, finding the right downloads to engage the younger mind isn't too difficult today thanks to a multitude of apps – ranging from games to interactive books – that have been designed to captivate children.

Lucy Ladybird is aiming to do just the same through its cute artwork and heart-warming story of a ladybird looking to fit in, and finding out that being different isn't so bad after all. While this is the obvious moral, it isn't heavy-handedly forced down the reader's throat at the detriment of the

story, and it's a tale that both parents and kids will surely enjoy interacting with together.

From a user experience perspective, Lucy Ladybird does a very good job of striking a balance when it comes to classic storytelling and taking advantage of the iPad's touchscreen. The story works on its own, but there is also the addition of some interactive features, like the ability to drag and drop spots onto Lucy, as well as animate other characters and the environment with a tap. Every page of the story has something interactive on it, and if it can't be immediately spotted there's a question mark icon that tells users where to tap in order to bring the page to life. Alongside this is a Home button that brings up a navigation bar

at the bottom of the screen, allowing users to jump to different pages as well as back to the main menu in just a single tap.

It can be argued that the interactivity within Lucy Ladybird is a little too simple given some of the things seen in other apps. Still, while the touch-triggered animation might be unspectacular at times, they do serve as a steady introduction for the younger users who are most likely to be drawn to this app.

A counter-argument to the interaction point is the presence of some of the fun extras beyond the main story section. There's a great colouring in section with six different pictures of characters from throughout the story to colour in by touching the screen. In fact, this section is something of a surprise package because the response and look of the brush strokes is very impressive for a non-creative app. This area of the app is a great place to let the kids loose in terms of

> "Lucy Ladybird does a very good job of striking a balance with classic storytelling and making the most of the touchscreen"

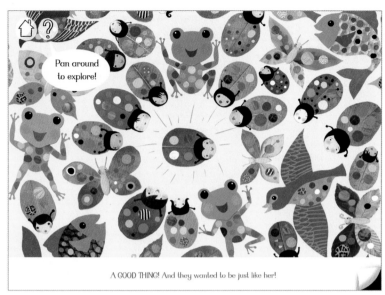

■ There are a host of fun and colourful characters that children will be introduced to throughout the interactive book

introducing them to the touchscreen, with a host of colours and a handy eraser. Should a little masterpiece appear, there's a Save option that gives users the chance to store drawings in Camera Roll for safekeeping.

If drawing isn't what the kids are looking for, there's also a Karaoke section that gives users the chance to put their own spin on the Lucy Ladybird theme song from the home screen. Complete with its own video of Lucy flying through different scenes and live lyrics on screen, this feels like a nice change of pace; a little more active and engaging. It also keeps kids from getting bored, as they will be able to apply themselves and get involved in more ways than one.

The App Store page says Lucy Ladybird is designed for children

aged two and up, and that is perfectly emphasised by the simplicity that app sticks with throughout the story. There is never too much dialogue and the artwork is wonderfully colourful, taking readers through each of the seasons with interactivity to bring each of them to life in fun yet simple ways. Lucy Ladybird then is a very good way to introduce youngsters to apps and the iPad without fear of them deleting any important files in the process. The extra features give kids a way of utilising any creativity that the app inspires as well.

Yes, compared to some other interactive books Lucy Ladybird is quite simple and potentially not on the same level in terms of content. Still, the app more than makes up for that with the level of charm it brings to the iPad screen through the moral-filled yet unimposing story, and the artwork that brings it to life, making it both visually and mentally engaging. If you're on the lookout for a new children's app, this might well be it.

**An endearing story with just enough animation to delight young iPad users and parents.**

■ This isn't just a story app - there are loads of activities to keep youngsters occupied

**01: The art**
Instantly engaging and charming to any user, the artwork feels classic and on the traditional side, while still engaging the younger users with bright colours.

**02: Text**
Nothing is more off-putting in a children's story than too much text. This app strikes the right balance, with enough happening in each scene without becoming a strain.

**03: Interactions**
On every page of the story is at least one interactive feature or animation. Some general tapping will usually uncover it, but there is also a handy hint button as well.

**04: Colouring in**
Away from the main story, there is also a great colouring section that gives kids the chance to colour in some of the main characters from the book in their own style.

**05: Karaoke**
For the extroverted, there is a karaoke mode that gives readers the chance to sing the theme song, that plays on the app's home screen. It's a great little feature in the app.

● Price £2.99/$4.99

# Jack and the Beanstalk

## The sky is the limit in this interactive fairy tale

Jack and the Beanstalk by Nosy Crow is an app that attempts to breathe new life into the classic fairy tale, blurring the line between interactive book and game. The presentation is top-notch, with beautifully drawn animated characters and excellent narration using children's voices. It's utterly charming and our young reader was soon captivated.

Tapping the characters makes them speak a good variety of phrases, so it doesn't get too repetitive. We were soon brushing and feeding the family cow, getting it ready for market, waiting for the little tune that indicates when it's possible to advance to the next scene – although you can do so at any time via an arrow. This comes in handy for a few scenes – such as walking the cow to market – which, rather bizarrely,

seem to go on forever. It all seems like a standard interactive story until you climb the beanstalk and reach the giant's castle. Here there are nine doors to unlock using coloured keys, each revealing a fun mini-game. These include lifting the dozing giant's arms to take coins, lowering a bucket down a well, mixing a foul soup and piecing together a mirror using the device's front camera to show your face, making full use of the iPad. The order of games is different each time and can result in various possible endings, increasing the replay and entertainment value for kids.

**Another polished Nosy Crow app that offers more involved gameplay than ever before.**

★★★★★

■ Jack and the Beanstalk blurs the line between interactive book and game

---

● Price £2.49/$3.99

# Mr Tickle Storybook app

## A delightful digital recreation of a classic

The legend that is Mr Tickle now lives on in a new storybook which offers a near perfect digital representation of the original book, alongside a selection of carefully thought out games to keep kids amused when they are bored. These games include colouring

in characters without the help of borders to create a realistic artistic environment, hitting worms in a non-aggressive way in timed levels and making funny faces using a selection of facial parts and objects. But it is in the storybook itself that the app truly shines.

The calming and perfectly paced narration complements the highlighted words to aid reading skills. From the moment the familiar music starts and Mr Tickle appears on screen, you and your children will be engrossed in the amusing storyline. In fact, it is highly debatable as to whether this storybook is best suited to children or to their parents who will most likely remember the Mr Men series with great fondness!

Every part of this app; from the charming graphics to the words make for an entertaining experience and it really is hard to fault a book that has been produced with such care. It is so good that it has the potential to introduce a whole new generation to the bizarre creation that is Mr Tickle and that is surely a very good thing.

**One of the most impressive recreations of a classic children's character we have seen yet.**

★★★★★

■ The imagery is completely authentic and extremely enjoyable to view

■ The included games will ensure that boredom is well and truly busted

■ Other characters exist in the game but cash is needed to unlock them

■ The options for customisation are endless, and allows for a lot of creativity

● Price Freemium

# Disney Infinity Toy Box
## Lots of Disney characters – but does it require lots of cash?

### PROS/CONS
▲ Building a new Disney world is great fun

▲ There are 50 items to use for free

▼ Controls are a tad too fiddly

▼ There are in-app purchases aplenty

With amazing visuals and a large array of Disney characters, this is an app that will not only instantly appeal to children but keep them occupied for days on end. It takes the Toy Box part of the console release and brings it to the iPad and, in doing so, unleashes a great deal of creativity – allowing players to do what they want, whenever they want.

First a word of warning to parents. There are in-app purchases, so if you want to avoid a shocking bill, make sure it is turned off in Settings. And now a warning to children: don't expect this to be a game that is handed to you on a plate. As gaming experiences go, this isn't a full-on arcade blast, rather a sandbox adventure that you create yourself.

You get a blank piece of land where you can create landscapes, place castles and various other elements. You can lay tracks to race around on and you can also use items collecting within the console game.

It doesn't take long before a world is being built up for the characters to charge around. But there is a problem: the controls are not the most user-friendly and you must keep an eye on the instructions that only appear once to get your head around the functions. Movement controls are also fiddly because too many buttons have been placed on the screen and get in the way.

But building and placing items on the landscape is easy and the 50 free pieces you get should be sufficient enough for most people. But that's where in-app purchasing comes in. To get more than Mr Incredible, for instance, the app requires money or codes that are included on retail toys.

**A free offering (if you avoid the in-app purchases) that has much to give as a standalone title, but is even better with the console game.**

★★★★★

■ Characters have special moves that are spectacular to watch

## "As gaming experiences go, it isn't a full-on arcade blast, but a sandbox adventure you create yourself"

● Price £2.99/$4.99

# Beauty and the Beast

 StoryToys has a habit of creating children's storybooks that bring the words and images to life in stunning 3D and it has done it again here. The interactivity is slightly more engaging this time around and young children will enjoy the mini-games as well as the ultimate goal, which is detailed in the story. It is of course suited more for little girls and the presentation is perfectly set to enchant them.

**A charming and brilliant storybook that will appeal most to girls.**

★★★★★

● Price £2.49/$3.99

# Alphabeasties

 This app does much more than merely present each letter in the alphabet, as the child can interact with the letters they guess correctly and to trace each one as part of a game. The subtlety of approach and proven effectivity is ideal for any child. The simplicity makes it a perfect educational tool.

**An imaginative learning tool to introduce the alphabet to young kids.**

★★★★★

● Price £0.69/$0.99

# Woodlander Tales

 Woodlander Tales is an interactive children's story. The animated elements that you tap almost make it feel like a game at times, but it is the clever recreation of the characters that make it stand out in a very crowded area of the App Store. Adults will appreciate the level of craft that has been put in to the visual interface and children will fall in love with the realism of the characters. A visually impressive and entertaining story.

**A fun experience for young children that can also be appreciated by adults.**

★★★★★

● Price £2.49/$3.99

# Doc McStuffins

 Many games on the app store claim to let your children play in a friendly and fun environment but few are as carefully created as this one. Here, children have the chance to cure characters of a variety of illnesses and all of the records are stored so that they can reflect on their achievements. The graphics are splendid with little room for confusion. The variety of the features and simplistic interface make it ideal for younger children.

**This children's game takes interactivity to a new level. It's a lot of fun.**

★★★★☆

● Price £2.99/$4.99

# Curious About Shapes & Colours

 This app uses the popular Curious George character to teach young children the basics about shapes and colours. The gradual increase in complexity is tailored perfectly to encourage children to learn with an emphasis on sensitivity and not making the experience feel like learning at all. Few apps are so focused on children – this one hits the mark.

**A brilliant way for children to learn without even realising they are.**

★★★★★

● Price £1.99/$2.99

# Pocket Universe

 In a galaxy of impressive astronomy apps, Pocket Universe's star shines brightest. Its interactive map of the night sky looks stunning and is highly customisable, enabling you to filter out various types of celestial objects. A search facility is completed by on-screen directions, and you can even ask the app questions like 'where does Jupiter set?'. You can also see what the sky will look like at a certain date and time, to help plan your stargazing.

**Visually it's top notch, and though its use is limited, it's very customisable.**

★★★☆☆

● Price £0.69/$0.99

# Jump Up and Join In

 The audio quality in this children's app is superb, with excellent narration throughout and some great musical games to add to the fun. Children will love the musical journey they're taken on. On a tablet it works particularly well with some of the graphical elements being slightly too small for a phone – but that should not detract from what is a clever diversionary and educational title.

**Any child who loves music or is a fan of the TV series will love this.**

★★★★☆

 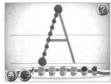

● Price £1.99/$2.99

# PLAY-DOH Create ABCs

 PLAY-DOH as a company is a universal concept, and its intentions with this app are admirable. Kids can use it to form letters and shapes, which works quite well and it's clear the implementation is designed specifically to teach, but it demands that the child has a good understanding of touchscreens. This seems to contradict the target age range, and could put off some users.

**Overall very good, but requires precise touchscreen handling.**

★★★☆☆

● Price £1.99/$2.99

# Toca Pet Doctor

 This game simulates a vet experience. Children need to feed the sick animals the appropriate cures and when they do, they get to play with them. The reward mechanism is just as well thought out as the splendid graphics, and the lack of any rules means that children of all ages can enjoy it. Whether you want to keep your child amused or just want to offer some fun, this works very well.

**Lots of surprises are in store for kids who get to use this app.**

★★★★★

● Price £1.49/$1.99

# Pettson's Jigsaw Puzzle

 As a puzzle game this one has all of the hallmarks required to make it a fun experience. The controls are easy-to-use and the visualisation is particularly good, which makes it feel like a real puzzle even on a smaller phone screen. Children and adults will enjoy the graphics and music, but the variety of puzzles needs to be much greater for it to captivate for a longer period of time. Still, it is very good at what it does and is worth a look.

**Entertaining, but it would benefit from more content to truly shine.**

★★★★★

● Price £1.49/$1.99

# Jim Henson's Chatter Zoo

 As a story this app works well, but it is the way its young audience can interact with the characters that lifts it even higher. Children get to feed the animals and even bathe them so that they get a genuine sense of looking after them. The graphics are just right and the sounds add to the experience, which helps keep children interested throughout. There is even an element of learning involved, which adds to a great all-round experience.

**An engrossing experience that will keep children happy.**

★★★★★

● Price £1.99/$2.99

# Wungi Pirates

 Wungi Pirates is a visually impressive children's app offering huge amounts of fun as the child navigates through the various screens. The games are challenging and interactive, the theme is fun and consistent, and the sense of achievement as the child succeeds is great, lifting the title above its rivals.

**This is a creatively designed app that should work very well with children.**

★★★★★

■ Almost every screen in the app is full of interactions of varying degrees

Sieve the flour into the bowl

■ Help Henri in his kitchen and then put his recipes to the test in your own

● Price £2.99/$4.99

# Henri Le Worm

## Simon Pegg teams up with a French culinary worm

### PROS/CONS

▲ Great story and characters to keep you entertained

▲ Intertwining recipes into the overall story is a great touch

▼ Some lag when trying to jump between pages

▼ Some of the navigation instructions aren't always clear

 A lot of emphasis is being put on food awareness in both adults and children today, and Henri Le Worm is an app that supports this through that popular genre of 'edutainment'.

Many apps have tried it in recent years across a broad range of subjects from human anatomy to maths and language skills. Henri Le Worm is taking things from a slightly different angle, looking to get users to be proactive, providing recipes and cooking methods for a host of the foods mentioned in the app. The idea is to get kids and their parents interested in food, but also the growing process – including the insects in your garden.

The app is built around the story of Henri Le Worm, an invertebrate chef

extraordinaire who's looking to win his garden's cooking competition. This is before his cookbook is stolen by the pesky Lumpy the Maggot, who's after the prize for himself. The story is narrated by comic actor Simon Pegg so instantly parents will have their interest twigged, and thanks to the interactivity, whimsical characters and vivid colours, the kids won't be bored anytime soon either.

The story makes an effort to touch upon some of the key areas of nutrition in an entertaining way, for example having the user make breakfast pancakes for Henri and his friends to highlight the most important meal of the day. It's at this point that another layer of the app's features appear – the recipes section. While you're helping

Henri flip virtual pancakes, the app asks you if you'd like to learn how to make them yourself. This links you to the recipes section, which is where Raymond Blanc takes over as master of ceremonies from Mr Pegg.

Although there is no narration from the chef, he does offer up some of his favourite family recipes, complete with guides, with certain steps within the instructions highlighted that are ideal for getting kids involved. There are some delicious dishes on offer, and most are mentioned somewhere in the story – nothing like some underlying hints to get you and your kids cooking.

While there are a couple of little bugs lurking within Henri Le Worm, there's nothing that can't be fixed in the first update; most issues relate to some lag when trying to navigate between pages, and overzealous interaction that sees a tap on an interactive point that happens to be hovering over a character bring them both to life. In general though, this is a

## "The narration is lively and interesting enough to keep you engaged, with Simon Pegg bringing his usual energy to proceedings"

There are also mini-games to play, including making and serving breakfast for Henri and his friends

very easy app to navigate – particularly with the clear controls on the screen combined with prompts from the narration to guide – which is a must for any app that wants to interact with children. There are also purple hot spots that appear to indicate a character or object on screen will react when tapped, and there are mini-games littered throughout the various screens within the app to keep the young minds occupied.

This app has done a great job of drawing users in thanks to its great use of colour from the outset; this is a very vibrant app from the moment you pick it up, and there is no doubt that kids will be drawn to it. Thankfully it has more than enough content to keep them occupied once they get here, and the story is balanced enough

to also be enjoyable, and potentially educational for adults too.

The narration is lively and interesting enough to keep you engaged, with Simon Pegg bringing his usual energy to proceedings and carrying off the range of voices and characters brilliantly. There's a great range of personalities throughout the story that younger users will want to interact with, and on pretty much every screen that is possible. Having been developed in part with Blanc's son, Olivier, some family inspiration has definitely gone into the creation of Henri as a character, and into making gastronomy much more accessible.

Henri Le Worm has done a brilliant job of standing out in a competitive field as well as being engaging throughout its usage time. The fusion of a fun narrative, celebrity collaboration, and manageable but tasty recipes is a brilliant way to get both adults and children back into the kitchen. Cooking is made fun again.

**A likeable app – and the practical side should keep you coming back often.**

Grow vegetables in the garden with Henri and his friends

## Showcase
## What is Henri's wow-factor?

If you look closely in any garden, park and forest there lives a secret world. If you look hard enough you can find the most wonderful things.

**01: The look**
As this is an app aimed predominantly at children, it needs to engage from the get-go, so Henri Le Worm has been design with an array of appealing and vivid colours.

**02: Characters**
There's a host of Henri's friends and enemies to meet and interact with throughout the story, with some providing educational content as well as some wonderful entertainment.

**03: Narrative**
This is designed primarily to entertain, but also has plenty of educational and engaging content running through it that is subtle enough to not turn you away.

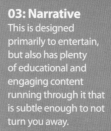

**04: Interactions**
Every screen within the app has something to interact with on varying levels, from simple soundboards right up to links for real recipes you can try out for yourself.

**05: Recipes**
Recipes are referenced throughout, and they also have their own dedicated section. Instructions also offer suggestions as to when kids can get involved in the cooking too.

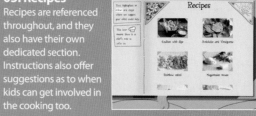

● Price £1.49/$1.99

# Monki Hide & Seek

 This app is a fun recreation of the classic hide and seek game, which can now be experienced on phones and tablets. The colours and animations are excellent, which should keep most children interested and involved throughout and, in our view, it offers very good value for money. In a crowded area of the app market, it stands out really well for the sheer quality and entertainment that's included.

**Young children will love the colours and harmless entertainment on offer.**

★★★★★

● Price £1.49/$1.99

# Toc And Roll

 Toc and Roll takes the idea of music creation and strips it down for young children, and presents it in a clear and easy way. And there's more. Throw in a selection of diverse, instantly recognisable instruments and near endless variety, and your children will be creating their own compositions in no time.

**Let your children create fun and original music.**

★★★★★

● Price £1.99/$2.99

# Dr. Panda's Toy Cars

 Do you remember the mats with roads on them that you played with as a child? The ones that transformed into a world of your own when you put a few toy cars on them? Well, this is the digital recreation and it comes with multiple vehicles with unique traits, challenges and all of the charm you could hope for. There is a lot of fun crammed into a small space here and children will adore having so much to play with.

**A brilliant children's game – well paced and adorable.**

★★★★★

● Price £1.99/$2.99

# Mr Shingu's Paper Zoo

 This app is a leading example of how to keep children entertained. It involves many fun activities, like creating origami animals and caring for them. What makes it a triumph is its colourful interface and the flexibility for children to make the app their own, so parents should appreciate the care that has gone into this child-centric masterpiece. It's one of the best children's mobile titles we've ever seen.

**Perfect for young children with lots of variety and many colours.**

★★★★☆

● Price £1.49/$1.99

# Squeebles Times Tables 2

 There is an art to teaching children their times tables. This app disguises the task as a game, making kids learn without even knowing they are. This way, they will likely learn a lot quicker and with more enthusiasm. There are rewards included and the presentation style used will appeal to younger children perfectly. Add to this a set of enjoyable mini-games and here we have a recipe for success.

**A subtle app that will help children enjoy learning their times tables.**

★★★★☆

● Price £1.99/$2.99

# Daniel Tiger's Day & Night

 Routines are important for children, especially at bedtime and in the morning. This app is designed to bring order to a child's day by using fun, colourful games accompanied by realistic sounds. The characters are friendly, which helps children subconsciously learn that routines are positive. This app is fun, but comes with a heavy dose of learning that both the child and parent can enjoy.

**A rewarding way for children to learn that routines can be useful.**

★★★★★

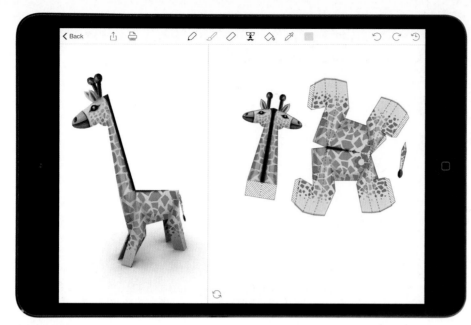

● Price £1.99/$2.99

# Foldify Zoo

## Get creative and design your own animal army!

With Foldify Zoo, you can create your own collection of animals decorated to your own design, made out of folded pieces of paper. From the makers of Foldify, it is a simple yet effective app that could provide hours of fun for children and adults alike. A Foldified Giraffe welcomes you to the app, along with geographical information and loads of extra educational information about the animal: providing creative entertainment as well as educational facts.

You can either choose and print the provided animal templates – via AirPrint or emailing a PDF to be printed – or let your creativity flow and give your animal a makeover. Be warned: this process can be a little tricky to get used to, and can feel a bit clunky and hard to navigate. It's not the end of the world when you make a mistake, though; you can simply tap undo.

The animals can be slightly fiddly to build once you have printed them out – there are three sizes available – so the bigger the better if you are all fingers and thumbs. It is worth persevering, though, as the end results are amusing and make great decorations!

**A romp of an app that offers hours of fun on and off the screen, despite offering challenges for clumsy fingers.**

★★★★☆

● Price £1.99/$4.99

# Walking with Dinosaurs: Inside their World

## A new app about old beasts proves a winner

With narration by Stephen Fry and so many wonderful 3D animations, this is the kind of app adults wished they had as a child. It brings dinosaurs to life: each screen oozing with information and visuals that teach so much about each different beast and how they lived in pre-human times.

An improved version of its predecessor, this app has enhanced graphics that take advantage of the Retina screen and has updated facts since science has developed. There are more than 60 animations in total with the features proving to be the most fun. Here you get to see the dinosaurs grabbing, chewing and discarding their prey, and you can also hear them – the app says they are original sounds, but obviously these were the result of expert guidance, helping to contextualise the images.

With 15 dinosaur hunters to read about and lots of well-researched articles on prehistoric life, this is an educational resource on a Jurassic scale. While it doesn't take long to read through everything, there are so many facts to digest that you will just have to keep going back.

**Photo-realistic dinosaurs and lots of facts combine to produce an educational app.**

★★★★★

■ Learn more dinosaur facts through detailed profiles

■ Access narration and page-turning controls

● Price £2.99/$4.99

# The Human Body

## Investigate your insides with this working model

 The Human Body by Tinybop is designed for anyone from the age of four and upwards, aiming to shows how our bodies work. An unusual feature is that it prompts you to create child and parent users when it is first used. The idea is that parents can view, save, and share conversations with their kids. However, it's not clear why you would need an app to do this and it offers no advice on how you would go about it or its benefits.

There is a panel on the left that looks like a menu showing different body parts, but it actually displays or hides layers, such as the nervous system, circulation system, skeleton and so on. This layered approach is interesting, but it is better when you view just an individual layer. Turn the labels on and you can see the names of organs, parts of organs and so on. Show the digestive system and you can drop food or drink into the mouth and watch it pass through the body. Zoom into the mouth and you can chew food and brush the teeth. Show the skeleton and the major bones are labelled. You can actually pull out the bones and then try to place them back in the right places in the body. The heart can be seen pumping and you can view it from the outside or as a cut-away diagram. You can even simulate running and see its effect on the heart, which is quite interesting.

User ratings for The Human Body by Tinybop in the App Store vary wildly betwen five or one star and this isn't surprising. For new users, it initially gives a poor impression with seemingly limited content. However, after using the app for some time, it's clear there is a lot more here than first meets the eye, but there are better alternatives out there.

**Despite its layered approach and diversity, it diappoints and fails to stand out amongst the competition. This is an average offering at best.**

★★★☆☆

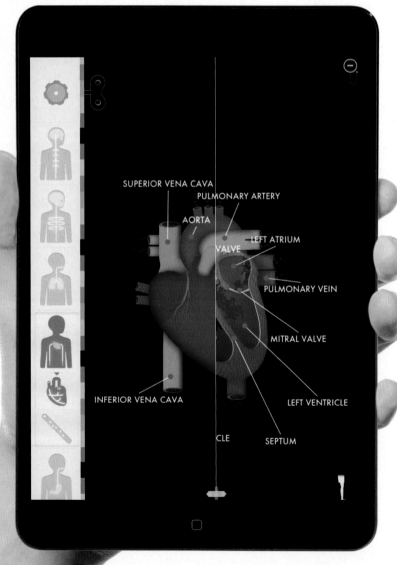

"You can even simulate running and see its effect on the heart, which is quite interesting"

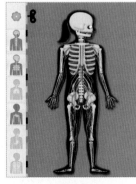

■ Layers can be added or hidden from view, allowing you to see how everything fits

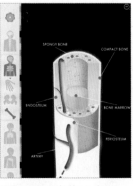

■ Zoom in to display a clear diagram and see all the nitty-gritty details

● Price £2.49/$3.99

# Odysseus For Kids
## The Odyssey has never been this fun and colourful

 Homer's The Odyssey, with its war sieges, vengeful gods, cave monsters and evil bird women, may not seem suitable education material for six-to-ten-year olds. But the way Odysseus For Kids makes this behemoth of mythology so accessible while keeping its war sieges, vengeful gods, cave monsters and evil bird women, is a testament to its tremendous quality.

Because The Odyssey is such an expansive poem, the decision to abridge it and narrate 15 beautifully animated tableaux of its major events keeps interest flowing throughout for us short-attention-span kids. Fun little challenges and puzzles to advance the story make the user feel a part of the adventure. You have to assemble the Trojan horse, lead Odysseus to his ship and more, through familiar jigsaw-puzzle, memory-matching and replay-the-melody formats. The design is flawless and the animations fit the story seamlessly.

Completing challenges earns you character portraits to put into an album, urging you to keep playing and make the ultimate collection. The absolute best bit, though, is the map. This design gem reveals real-world locations of these mythical happenings, lending a sense of relatability, and providing a geography lesson at the same time.

**The best kind of education app; one where you have too much fun to notice you're learning.**

★★★★★

■ The app's design helps to engage the imagination

■ Earn character portraits through completing challenging mini-games

● Price £1.99/$2.99

# Dino Walk: Continental Drift
## See the world the dinosaurs walked

 Your mobile device as a time machine is one of its biggest strengths, with the wealth of knowledge that science has uncovered over the years, developers have huge amounts of information to play with. Presenting it in engaging ways has been what separates the notable apps from the best, and while the interactive globe that also serves as a timeline within Dino Walk is a great spectacle, this app feels as if it falls slightly short in terms of the content it offers.

The premise and skeleton of the app is good, including an interactive 3D globe that users can zoom in and out of, and touch points of various creatures and plants of note for users to read about. This starts to include extinct species as you move through time periods. While it is engaging to see how the planet's landmasses have moved and changed over time, the single image and paragraph that comes with each creature feels limited. While youngsters will be grasped by the polished interface and images, their attention might begin to wane soon after.

There is a quiz to test the knowledge picked up from the flashes of text, but it won't sustain you for long. It was a promising start, but Dino Walk stumbled.

**Good on the surface with a slick interface, but lacking the depth to ever be considered great.**

★★★★★

■ Images are beautiful and vibrant, though slightly static and limited

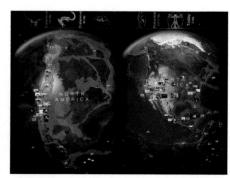
■ Choose where to learn about dinosaur history from a detailed globe map

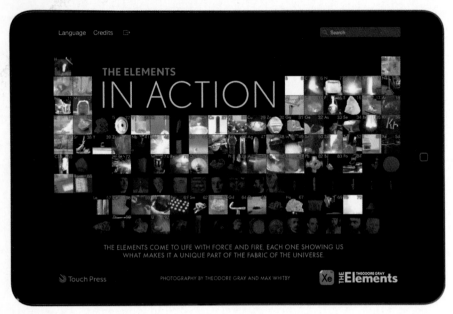

■ Each element has a high-quality video explaining its properties

■ The opening screen presents you with a visual representation of the periodic table

● Price £2.49/$3.99

# The Elements in Action

## Watch the periodic table come to life

Educational apps are relatively common, but few are as richly and uniquely presented as The Elements in Action. The premise is simple in that you are given a series of animated elements on the attractive main navigation screen and tapping each will lead to a video that starts playing immediately. The included videos will either show the element being created or demonstrate an experiment using the element in question.

Each video also includes a brief description below the main screen, so you also get an overview of the science behind the explosive experiments. However if you choose to also buy The Elements: A Visual Exploration, its sister app, the two downloads work together and the possibilities to learn about the periodic table grow exponentially.

Once combined, tapping on a spinning icon in The Elements in Action will take you to the element listing in A Visual Exploration so you can read about various properties including the atomic radius, melting point and percentages. The Elements in Action is a superb title on its own, but if you use both the apps in tandem they will create a solution that suits both academics and the curious in equal measure.

Even with all of the educational features that form the core of the app, it is in the presentation that it truly shines. The wonderful start screen with animated elements gives way to videos that play without any delay and there is a sense that this app should be a model for others to follow. The attention to detail is so comprehensive that it feels as if it is from the future. Yet here it is, ready to give you a wonderful experience and teaching you a little along the way.

**Impressively educational on its own, but it can easily be made to work as part of a dynamic duo. Absolutely stunning.**

★★★★★

■ The main navigation screen is animated and looks fantastic

"The attention to detail is so comprehensive that it feels as if it is from the future, yet here it is"

● Price Free

# MarcoPolo Ocean

This app is effectively a 'place the object' game for young children, but it is one that attempts to inform them about the oceans and the creatures that live within them. The narration is very friendly and the background music adds a playful tone, but together it all works perfectly to create a place for any child to relax and learn. This is also perfect for the iPad's high quality screen, as the animations are very clear and colourful.

**An absorbing and friendly app for children and adults.**

★★★★★

● Price £1.99/$2.99

# Tilly and Friends

Tilly and Friends is a popular TV show and the experience has been transferred well to an app with all of the personality and fun intact. There are many different games to play and most children will have no problem understanding what to do, but it does work better on a tablet screen. The simple games will keep kids happy and educated for hours, and has kept the charm that made the TV show so loved amongst children.

**A selection of games that are educational, fun and well presented.**

★★★★☆

● Price £5.99/$8.99

# The In Gen

children's titles will be... the future, but it is doing it now. Very young children get to control Harvey the dog as he meanders through space and meets other characters while interacting with various objects that he will find lying around. The sounds and graphics are spot on and it is a joy to use and watch, showing the effort that has gone into making it. Kids will love this! Parents get downloading now.

**An immersive and brilliant virtual toy for younger children.**

★★★★★

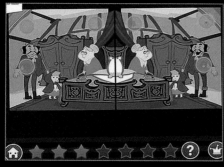

● Price £1.49/$1.99

# 7 differences

Young children are likely to love the simplicity of this game and the way it taxes their minds in a gentle way. The classic spot-the-difference games are included alongside memory games, as well as an unusual mirror game which offers a new perspective to train young minds to think in a different way.

**A fairly impressive spot-the-difference game that'll appeal to young children.**

★★★★★

● Price £1.99/$2.99

# Slice Fractions

The visuals in Slice Fractions immediately make it feel like yet another puzzle game, and that is what it can be if that's what you're after specifically. However, put it in the hands of children and they will be treated to an educational experience that feels more like fun than any lesson possibly could. The varied physics puzzles will help teach them fractions in no time at all.

**It feels like a game, but has a subtle educational element and is fun to play.**

★★★★★

● Price £4.99/$6.99

# Write to Read

In this app, children get to create their own books based on any subject, which automatically helps them to read and write. The options are numerous and the output realistically portrays what the child has created, which makes it fun for parents. It is innovative and could make all the difference to your child's perspective on reading and writing.

**A very clever solution which makes learning to read and write fun.**

★★★★★

# Incomplete Map of the Cosmic Genome

## Marvel at the universe with Brian Cox, Robin Ince and more

Many of us cannot resist a glance upwards at the stars on a particularly clear night; curiosity is a part of the human condition. The Incomplete Map of the Cosmic Genome is an app that celebrates our wide-eyed wonder by bringing together a collection of scientists, writers and performers to talk about the things they love about science and the universe we inhabit.

It's a unique angle to approach the App Store at, but there is no doubting the appeal once you begin watching all of the short videos. Whether it is celebrity physicist Professor Brian Cox discussing his earliest memories of science, Richard Dawkins on biology, or comedian Stewart Lee explaining gravity to his young son, there is a mixture of both knowledge and entertainment to be gained.

The introduction video from comedian Robin Ince leads you to a periodic table of contributors, each one of them talking about the field of science they find the most fascinating. Every profile comes with a short video as well as a transcript. Users can choose to stream content or download it, so it's always accessible, even offline.

There is also a special topics section, which is a selection of short videos on a single topic by the same guests. The app offers an impressive range of content, balancing hard science with observational humour. The gaps on the periodic table screen hint at the promise of future videos.

Cosmic Genome has a slightly unconventional structure in that it requires a subscription to receive the new content each month. Outside of magazine apps this is rare, but curiosity might just get the better of you.

> "There is no doubting the appeal once you begin watching all of the short videos"

**If you're thirsty for knowledge and discussion then this app is most definitely for you, but you have to be willing to pay for what you get.**

★★★★★

■ The information section links to the app's website, so you can see all the latest news

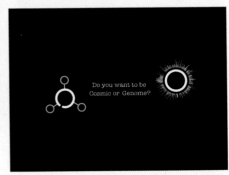

■ There's a short introductory video to get you up to speed with what to expect from the app

Professor Brian Cox

■ You'll see all kinds of familiar faces and renowned scientists retell stories and experiences

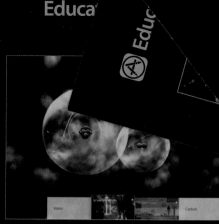

■ Use the app to explore or brush up on your knowledge of the Elements

■ The app offers some beautiful imagery of animals from all over the world

● Price £3.99/$5.99

# Brian Cox's Wonders of Life

## An incredible 3D journey to uncover the secrets of life

This is an absolutely breathtaking exploration of the building blocks of life spread across 1,000 images, more than 2 hours of video and over 80 engaging articles. Professor Brian Cox explains everything from the speed of animals to the origin of the senses by whisking you off to distant places, such as Christmas Island and the Mohave Desert, to unearth how physics underpin the laws of nature. For an added layer of interaction, 30 of the images are rendered in stunning 3D and can be zoomed in on to explore in depth.

To navigate the app, you use the large globe to select a continent, or top toolbar to select topics, such as Sensory, Microscopic, or Elements & Processes. Tap on the bottom thumbnails to view more information about the place or topic, as well as images and videos. Cox's own personal anecdotes keep the articles and videos light and entertaining, and the crisp high-res images and HD video make for an immersive experience.

The interactive experience can, at times, be a little confusing. It's not always obvious where you need to tap to trigger an action, or where that might take

you. As you scroll down through an article, videos and images automatically open to full-screen, which can be frustrating if you're still reading the text above it. It's also disappointing that you're forced to register your email address to access 'bonus' content, but this is optional.

Wonders of Life is such a comprehensive and engaging app, whatever your level of interest going in, you'll find something to be mesmerised by.

---

**Despite challenging navigation, it is fun to get lost and be immersed alongside Earth's lifeforms. The sheer amount of content alone is worth it.**

★★★★★

■ Tap the thumbnails to learn more about a topic

"You are whisked off to distant places… to unearth how physics underpin nature"

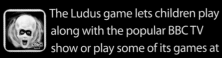

● Price Free

# Ludus

 The Ludus game lets children play along with the popular BBC TV show or play some of its games at another time. The presentation is perfect for children and every aspect is colourful and easy to use. However, there are a few bugs in the latest version, which is a shame as it does everything it needs to very well.

**A clever app that lets children interact with the TV show, but with bugs.**

★★★★★

● Price £9.99/$13.99

# The Liszt Sonata

 This app is somewhat specialist as it will work best in the hands of those who already have a musical background and knowledge. It shows Liszt's Piano Sonata in B Minor being played from multiple camera angles and also includes extras such as an interactive score and a selection of video insights. It's well presented and suits the subject matter perfectly in the way the elements are put together, despite its limited audience.

**Beautiful, educational and fun. What more could you want from an app?**

★★★★★

● Price £1.99/$2.99

# Chore-inator

Chore-inator is a useful tool for parents who struggle to get their children to do their chores. It lets users build in rewards to provide more incentive and use photos and a schedule to make the process feel less like work. Though some may find it rigid, if users stick to it, it should make life easier for everyone.

**A visual way to keep children focused on their chores that actually works.**

★★★★★

● Price £1.99/$2.99

# Curious George's Town

You could easily be mistaken for thinking that Curious George's Town is a children's book, but once you start looking deeper you realise that it is a very immersive game. There is a lot to do here and the graphics are simple enough for young children to understand, with an emphasis placed on learning and thinking about the environment. It is similar to some other games, but it's well worth the price and should keep kids entertained for a long time.

**An entertaining game that will appeal to children of all ages.**

★★★★☆

● Price £1.99/$2.99

# Toca Builders

 Toca Builders is like Minecraft for children, and you can build just about anything. You'll soon erect lavish constructions from a bare landscape, controlling little robots with different skills. There is also a destructive element as you smash blocks to make new constructions, which used to be a blast with Lego too.

**Like comparing Duplo to Lego, but this mini Minecraft will get kids creating.**

★★★☆☆

● Price £1.49/$1.99

# Skylanders Cloud Patrol

 This game may look like it was designed for children, but as you dig deeper you realise there is a lot of depth here – and it is this that makes the game very addictive. There is a sense of achievement throughout and despite the in-app purchases, you can progress quite easily without having to spend money. As you shoot the aliens and practise moves, you'll find great satisfaction in killing more. It's not original, but it's very good.

**A classic shooter with entertaining graphics and addictive qualities.**

★★★★☆

● Price Freemium

# Journeys of Invention

## It's your very own hands-on science museum

Part educational, part entertainment, this app showcases science at its fascinating full potential. Drawing on 80 objects from London's Science Museum, it allows users to explore 14 interactive stories that bring them to life, allowing you to examine and discover them in a very compelling manner.

Initially, we thought the app was taking rather a long time to load until we realised that the many little images on what appeared to be the title screen could be tapped and enlarged. By pinching to zoom in on this screen, the images can be seen in greater detail but you can also make out the lines that link the various objects together.

Like a subway map, all of these items are connected according to their type on colour-coded lines. Subjects include Industrial Adventures, Secrets of Life, Mass Production and many more. Each line will take you on a multimedia journey with text, images and, in some cases, video, making the app as visual as it is informative.

There are numerous little quirky animations included and some of them really raise a smile. We loved the way the entry for the Roomba 780 would display a little

robotic vacuum cleaner moving around the screen, clearing away the text, for example. All of the entries have movement of some kind, whether it's being able to rotate an Apple I computer or swiping at a globe to send it spinning around.

This gives a very hands-on feel to the app and it's as if you are in the museum with permission to play. The text that accompanies each entry is well written and short enough to stave off boredom, and there are also little fact files that present more of a snapshot view of items too.

The photos are also well chosen and atmospheric, adding to the visual experience of the app. Each one is explained and you can zoom in and out to see them in more detail. They also include some contemporary artworks that are rarely seen, which makes for a more complete package.

**We had as much fun exploring this app as we have when visiting the real-world museum, without leaving our seats. Brilliant.**

★★★★☆

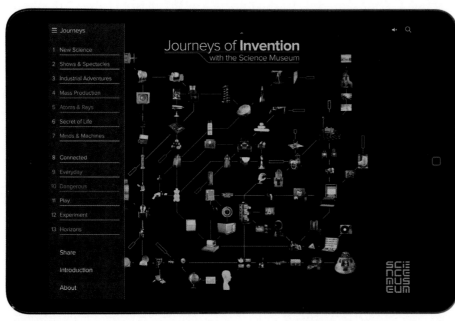

See the different categories of inventions and how they are all linked with each other

■ Explore all the inventions through text, images or get interactive

■ There is just the right amount of text to keep people from getting bored

"There are numerous little quirky animations included which raise a smile"

● Price £2.99/$4.99

# NHM Alive

## David Attenborough breathes new life into extinct animals

A spin-off from David Attenborough's recent Sky TV programme set in the National History Museum, this app offers its own educative excitement. At first glance, there's not much going on as you swipe between fossilised exhibits of ten extinct animals, but dig a little deeper and you'll discover a treasure trove of information complemented by some CGI to bring the beasts back to life.

In the default day mode, with its static photos, a pull-out menu lets you view information on the current exhibit, including how and where it was discovered – interesting, if a little dry. A timeline shows you when all ten animals became extinct. You can also bring up a rotatable 3D map of the museum, where you can input symbol codes – found in the real museum when you visit – for six of the exhibits to unlock extra video clips.

However, it's when you swipe down the screen to move into night mode that things become a bit more exciting – and rather eerie, reminiscent of the Night At The Museum movies. Each exhibit starts off shrouded in darkness until you hold your finger on the screen to shine a torch, thereby revealing a CGI animation of the animal and starting an audio commentary about it by Attenborough. There are also different options in the sidebar menu for night mode, including a view of the security camera room. The second option brings up bite-size facts and figures about the animal, while the final option reveals a media library for the animal; along with stills and clips from the TV show, this includes 3D models that you can swipe to rotate and see the animated CGI animal walk or fly – giving you a better idea of how it moved.

> "You'll discover a treasure trove of information complemented by CGI to bring the beasts to life"

**A highly educational app whose spooky night mode and CGI animations make it more exciting and engaging for children.**

★★★★★

■ Shine the torch in night mode to reveal the CGI animal and start an audio commentary

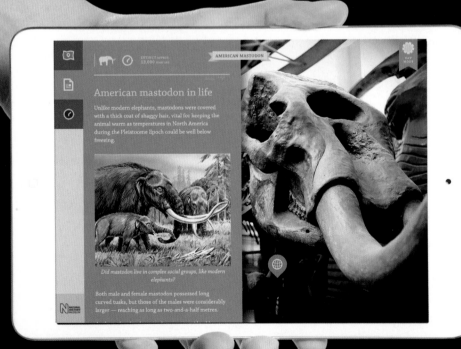

■ Day mode offers interesting textbook-style information about the ten featured exhibits

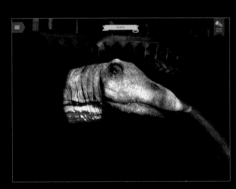

■ The security office view spookily offers fleeting glimpses of the animals on the monitors

● Price £2.49/$3.99

■ And so it starts. One tap of the green book and you are into the story

■ The story, characters and illustrations are sure to evoke nostalgia

# Charlie Brown's All Stars!

## Snoop around this adventure with everyone's favourite kid

**PROS/CONS**

▲ The story is a classic one of friendship

▲ The visuals and characters feel very authentic

▼ It could do with some more interactivity

▼ It is not clear from the start that it is interactive

Charlie Brown's adventures have endured for a long time and while there are lots of cartoon strips and TV episodes, few really bring him to life in the same way as this interactive app. While you cannot do too much with the characters on the screen, there is enough to keep even the most easily bored children going.

The classic story revolves around friendship and the fostering of team spirit is as much a learning process as it is an actual yarn of the story. There is an educational feel to the proceedings and a pervading sense of emotion as you go through the book. You can use the iPad to tilt and swipe on the screen and get involved with the action to a degree. You can swing a bat, catch a ball or touch the characters and have them slide, move and wobble around.

All the time you have great narration from Stephen Shea who is the voice of Linus van Pelt, and work has been done to bring the original illustrations, voices and music together too. This story is based on the animated TV special from 1966 so there is a massive dollop of authenticity and nostalgia.

And that is what makes it so special. It's less the interaction and more the fact that it is something both parents and

children can enjoy. There's also a learning process going on with being able to turn the narration on and off, have words highlighted or tap on a word to hear it spoken. The app's illustrated style also takes full advantage of the screen.

All of this ensures that the Charlie Brown stories endure and remain relevant to today's audience. It's not a short book so it'll last, leaving you with a feeling that you can go back over it again and again. It's definitely a worthwhile purchase.

**The tale makes for a good bedtime story or a great way to see this childhood favourite come to life with modern technology.**

★★★★★

NARRATOR: The team stormed off the field.

■ The characters are brought back to life in a classic style

> "It's less the interaction and more the fact that it is something both parents and children can enjoy"

● Price £2.99/$4.99

# Capo Touch
## Play your guitar along to any song you like

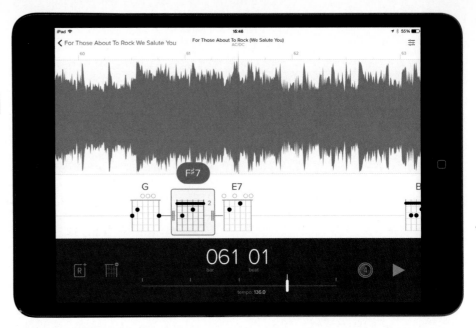

Replacing the original Capo song-learning app for guitar players, this brand new version offers some interesting extra features. The most notable of which is automatic chord detection. Load up a song from your music library and the app will attempt to detect the chords, placing them underneath the waveform of the music so you can play along with it.

Sadly, this potentially killer feature doesn't work all that well and tends to miss out quite a few chords while getting others wrong. Fortunately, you are able to insert missing chords (with the tap of a button at a point in the music) and amend wrong ones, but it's a bit of a faff when you just want to get on with learning to play a song. There's no facility for adding guitar tabs either, just chords, so it's not much use for learning riffs. On the plus side, you can activate a count-in, slow down the music, reduce the volume of vocals (with a neat adjustable frequency range) and loop sections that you want to practise. There's also a choice of various stringed instruments – including banjo, mandolin and ukelele – with adjustable tunings and capo fret positions. With all these options at hand, it's quite a versatile tool. Another plus is the ability to sync song data to iCloud and share it with the Mac version of the app.

**The automatic chord detection is disappointing, but this could still prove a useful song-learning tool.**

★★★☆☆

● Price £1.49/$1.99

# Caspar Babypants Music Time!
## Musical entertainment for toddlers and parents

After founding an American rock band, performing world tours and selling countless albums, Chris Ballew found himself a new career under the name Caspar Babypants. He has six music albums and now an iPad app. They're all aimed at kids and encourage them to enjoy music and play along.

The home screen provides access to the albums and you get two songs from each one with the app. If you already own any of the albums or buy them, the app is then able to play any of the songs on the iPad.

When the music starts there are three instruments to choose from that enable you to play along. A xylophone and guitar are available. You don't need to know anything about music because the instruments can only play notes from the song's chords. As the chords change, so do the notes and you can tap the xylophone and pick or strum the guitar strings in any order, or you can tap along on the drums.

In addition to the instruments, there is one more option and that is to display the lyrics as they are sung. You and your child can sing along, make music and have fun.

**A different way for parents and children to experience music and spend some time together.**

★★★★☆

■ A drum kit lets you get creative with the beat

■ The app is throughtfully aimed at younger children, featuring a dedicated baby mode

● Price £1.99/$2.99

# Shakespeare300

## Concise summaries and resources for all of the Bard's plays

Even scholars of the Bard's writings can struggle to remember plot details and themes across all of his works. Shakespeare300 offers concise, 300-word plot summaries and introductory notes for every play Shakespeare wrote, so if you're cramming for an exam or just want a handy overview to refer to, then you're going to be interested in this.

The notes themselves – from established American author James Reese – are engaging, succinct and entertaining to read. It's no replacement for a proper study aid or book of criticism, of course, but as 300-word summaries go these are hard to beat. Only a handful of times does the word limit create an awkward phrasing.

Each play has four pages covering the main themes, the plot, an infographic overview and a character map. There are some useful extras here too, including a timeline of the Bard's life and work, and less serious content like the top 15 Shakespearean insults.

The app isn't the most well-presented we've ever seen, but it gets the job done, and the visualisations and character maps are executed well. The front page sorts the plays into tragedy, history, romance and comedy for easy reference. Seasoned Shakespearean scholars will probably turn their noses up at Shakespeare300 but in our modern age of bite-sized information, it's a useful resource to have at your disposal if you have any interest in the playwright. If you're heading off to a production of one of these plays, for example, Shakespeare300 could be a good way to refresh your memory on some of the characters and plot points involved. There are spoilers, but you could skip the Plot page for the play in question.

**A easily digestible primer on the works of the famous Bard, though it can't replace a study aid or - heaven forbid - the real thing.**

★★★★★

> ## "The notes themselves are engaging, succinct and entertaining to read"

■ The refers to all of Shakespeare's most famous and beloved plays

■ The layout of the front page looks a lot like a periodic table of the Bard's theatrical works

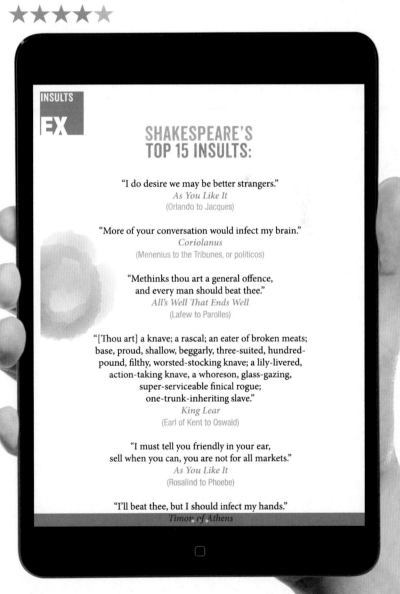

# Games
## Make your iPad the ultimate portable console

"The iPad's controls make for a unique game experience"

All the great villains of the DC universe are here for you to take on and defeat

One-tap battles are great pieces of action; just be sure to tap on the bad guys

● Price £2.99/$4.99

# LEGO Batman: DC Super Heroes

## Who can say no to a LEGO Justice League?

### PROS/CONS

▲ 80 playable characters is more than enough to delight DC fans

▲ Sticks true to the Lego game design; as fun as ever

▼ Touch control system can be horribly inaccurate

▼ Will take up quite a lot of space on your device

 Comic-book heroes are all the rage today, with more Justice League movies in the works. And with the last few years having been dominated by Marvel character movies, the time to be a super-hero fanatic is now. LEGO Batman: DC Super Heroes feels like a celebration of this era, bringing together a vast array of playable characters alongside Batman and Robin (the main protagonists), to take down just about every DC universe bad guy you can possibly think of.

Anyone familiar with the Lego way of gaming will be right at home here, as DC Super Heroes, like the other Lego ports we've seen on iOS, follows the usual pattern of combining plenty of platforming with puzzles and fighting off bad guys. All the while you gather studs that can be used to unlock more playable characters as you move through the game. Controlling the characters is another issue, however, and something that has cropped up in the Lego game series in the past. While this is the first touch-screen port to offer users a choice between on-screen buttons and gesture-based controls, the latter can be unpredictable and inaccurate when you're trying to differentiate between tapping the environment or an enemy. It's a hitch that you never fully get past, even as you settle into the game and the controls, and it will likely frustrate you as you play.

Although this could be somewhat of an issue, the controls shouldn't and won't stop you from enjoying the game, which has some really great cut-scenes complete with new and original dialogue and talking minifigs (unfortunately not voiced by Christian Bale, Adam West, Michael Keaton, or any other actors from the Batman movies, but a gamer can dream), both firsts for Lego gaming on iOS. On the subject of new things, DC Super Heroes has some new upgrades for players to look out for, with new suits for the Dynamic Duo to increase their powers and unleash special abilities needed to complete different puzzles. It's exciting for any DC fan to see their heroes in a new skin, and being able to expand your powers at the same time is a very nice bonus.

It's also worth watching out for golden bricks, which are included as

## "DC Super Heroes combines platforming with puzzles and fighting off bad guys"

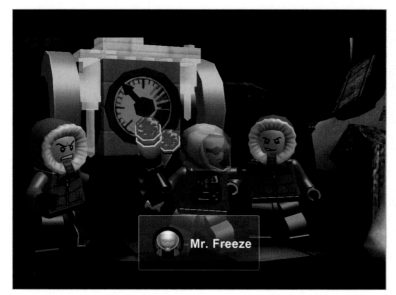

If only Schwarzenegger voiced Mr. Freeze again: "What killed the dinosaurs? The Ice Age!"

## Showcase
### Holy smokes, LEGO Batman!

**01: The Dynamic Duo**
As is traditional within the Lego gaming franchise, you will jump between characters to complete levels, creating a diverse experience.

**02: Platforming**
A big aspect of the game is 3D platforming, using your skill (and Robin's finesse) to reach new parts of each level. Get ready to get crafty and creative to complete every level.

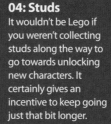

**03: Puzzles**
As well as running around, fighting the Joker and so on, there's a constant stream of puzzles to solve, as you would expect from a game that's made out of building blocks.

**04: Studs**
It wouldn't be Lego if you weren't collecting studs along the way to go towards unlocking new characters. It certainly gives an incentive to keep going just that bit longer.

an alternative form of payment when it comes to unlockables, should you still be short of studs. This is a logical step for the mobile version, where playing times and attention spans are far shorter, so players want rewards quicker. They're hard to come by, but gathering bricks is a very handy way to bypass hoarding studs when you want to unlock something, and comes with the territory of any Lego game.

As a full port of a console game, DC Super Heroes is a fairly sizeable download, requiring 2.6GB if done over WiFi which, if you're a big gamer, potentially means having to clear some space before you start the purchase process. But at £2.99/$4.99 you are getting a lot of game, and both Lego and DC fans won't be disappointed with what they have to play with

in terms of character base and environments to work through. There's full voice acting for the first time, and it gives the whole game more of an individual identity than previous Lego titles, which can simply feel like Lego versions of existing stories. This is an original story, albeit an exaggerated and frantic one where a different super villain awaits in every room, but that's what a fun game is all about; doing battles with those whom you love to hate, combined with the fun gimmick that everything is Lego. There's a reason this franchise has been so successful.

Yes, users may have to grit their teeth at times because of the control imperfections, but touch-screen gaming – particularly ports of console games – is still far from an exact science, and given the rest of the world you enter when you play this game, it feels like a trade-off you're happy to accept because of the enjoyment you'll have over the many levels, via the many characters.

**A roaring sequence of fantastic characters, both good and evil, that will thrill every DC fan.**

★★★★☆

Who wouldn't recognise some of DC's most famous characters?

Hey, Batlame and Slobbin. Why are you guys hanging around? Ha! See what I did there...

**05: Bad guys**
As well as all those super heroes, every nemesis you could ask for is here and ready to try and take out Batman and co. It all makes for a great game.

● Price **Free**

# Avengers Alliance

## Assemble your own team of iconic superheroes

 Have you ever wondered what it would be like to run S.H.I.E.L.D.? Well, Avengers Alliance gives you a taste for it in a game that is part Football Manager, part turn-by-turn battle game.

The game sees you taking control of a new agent within the CIA for superheroes, patrolling the skies over New York City. Various missions pop up as you move between the 2D areas of the city, with Avengers to unlock as you fight alongside them. Once you've started unlocking them, the management aspect kicks in as you can trade Avengers in and out of your battle team, as well as send them on training missions to level up.

In terms of the gameplay, this isn't the 3D epic fighter that the Avengers universe could lend itself to. Still, the turn-by-turn strategy battles don't tire, and the animations on each attack are more than enough to keep you satisfied visually.

The real thrill remains with the bossing around the iconic Avengers heroes, tweaking your squad as you see fit. But fans of other Marvel characters need not despair – X-Men and the Fantastic Four aren't ignored. This is a great time-killer and the management aspect captures the imagination.

**Totally delivers with a great range of characters and immersive gameplay. Prepare to be addicted.**

★★★★☆

---

● Price **£0.69/$0.99**

# Darklings

## An action-puzzle game that is hot on symbols

 If there is one thing that's essential to a good mobile game, it's the controls. Get it right and the game will reward the player. Get it wrong and, no matter how beautiful it is, it will fail. Darklings, thankfully, is of the former camp.

Not only does it look amazing with its atmospheric black and white design but, in asking the player to draw a series of symbols on the screen – each one matched to a baddie that needs to be possessed – it stands out for its ingenuity. You don't have to be mega precise with the scribbles either, which is a good thing when the action hots up and the baddies come thick and fast, as you'll be scribbling frantically.

When an enemy is killed, stars appear. Collecting these by running your finger over them in a path towards your main character will then enable you to buy some power-ups later on. It is also possible to buy bundles of stars with hard cash through in-app purchases.

There are boss battles too, which require you to doodle complicated patterns of symbols to defeat them. This increase in difficulty jars a little with the rest of the game, but it will reward an accomplished player. The game takes a long time to lose its freshness, it's something that will keep you coming back.

**Darklings is an amazingly addictive game that makes full use of the touchscreen capabilities.**

★★★★★

■ You need to draw symbols on the screen in order to inhabit enemies

■ Collect stars once a foe has been killed for power-ups and extra goodies

● Price £2.99/$4.99

# LEGO Marvel Super Heroes: Universe in Peril
### How not to port a console game to a tablet...

 The LEGO Marvel Super Heroes game (minus the Universe in Peril suffix) released to critical and commercial success last winter; operating around a New York hub world in between missions, players could do anything they wanted during non-story gameplay. The corridor-led level design was broken up in the hub, allowing the player to be anarchic and free, wreaking havoc on New York's docile inhabitants as your favourite heroes or heroines.

Unfortunately, the iOS and handheld console ports of the game took this vital facet of the game away, leaving the player with a slew of linear, repetitive missions that don't bring anything new to what LEGO Lord of the Rings was doing on iOS years ago. The option to play

as any of the Marvel heroes you'd recognise from the cinematic universe is certainly a draw, and the fan-service in the game will prompt smiles from Marvel aficionados, but clunky handling and lack of imagination on the designer's part will quickly make this game feel like a chore, rather than a treat. Seeing each hero's unique moves and animations is fun, but with a roster comprised mostly of pallet swaps, even that becomes tiresome after a few hours.

At £2.99/$4.99, you're getting a much better deal than the 3DS or Vita versions of the game (each retailing at £30/$50). However, the economy of unlocks and super moves (the best parts of the game) are skewed in favour of in-app purchases. You can complete the game without paying more, but it's a far more boring experience.

> ## "Seeing each hero's unique moves is fun, but even that becomes tiresome after a while"

**Comic book fans will find a lot to enjoy, but this slipshod port has turned the tried-and-tested LEGO formula into something that doesn't work.**

★★★☆☆

■ Get involved in some of the most memorable battles from comic books and movies

■ The tablet game really struggles to render the LEGO pieces effectively

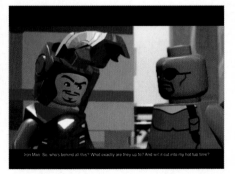

■ The cutscenes will raise a smile amongst Marvel comic book and movie fans

■ Lumber is important so that you can fill the depot with materials

■ Watch out, a burglar's about so you need to get some law and order

● Price £2.99/$4.99

# 1849

## Classic management game sprinkled with gold

### PROS/CONS

▲ Building schools, churches and saloons is fun

▲ It's intuitive, challenging and well-presented

▼ There is no sandbox mode

▼ It can be a tad on the repetitive side

There are moments in 1849 that prove to be genuinely stressful; times when you feel your heart beating because things aren't going quite right. Whether it is because goals are not being met or you actually care what happens to the citizens of 1849 California at the height of the Gold Rush, it makes for quite a compelling experience.

For those who have never played a city-management sim before, the basic idea is that you create towns and attract workers to them. To retain them, you must make them happy by building lots of houses, ensuring they have somewhere to go to rest – typically the saloon, and giving them plenty of food. Revenue must keep flowing, so you can sell brandy to prospectors in other towns and make and sell bread and other things. Citizens need the means to be self-sufficient to a degree, so you hope they don't starve, downgrade their homes and flee.

Unlike many games of this type, the complex gameplay is made up of levels with specific targets. It is these that put the pressure on. Robbers put a spanner in the works ensuring you need sheriffs, earthquakes can shatter infrastructure and fires can break out. While the actual gameplay is repetitive, it doesn't always feel like it because

you're moving from different scenarios, be it spartan camps or cramped cities.

Key to the game seems to be to overcompensate: building more houses to attract more people than you can employ, generating more money than you can spend, that sort of thing, something that is present in similar games. There is a sense of stabbing at the screen during panic moments, not quite sure of what you're doing, but due to its slick presentation, 1849 is a surefire winner despite the dents that might start appearing in your screen.

**With a lengthy campaign and lots to keep you on your toes, 1849 achieves gold. The price is worth the realistic experience.**

★★★★☆

■ The town is developing and you have an operating olive press

## "The complex gameplay is made up of levels with specific targets that put the pressure on"

● Price £2.99/$4.99

# Gemini Rue

## Solve the mystery to free the galaxy in this sci-fi noir

The genre cross-pollination of science fiction and noir detective stories has produced many great results, most famously the cult classic movie Bladerunner. New release Gemini Rue seeks to continue this trend.

Also available on PC as a point-and-click adventure, Gemini Rue's controls appropriate the same system using the touch screen, so that you tap on items and characters to interact through options like Look, Touch, Kick and Speak. This genre of gameplay has worked successfully on iOS with the likes of Machinarium and recent release The Silent Age, but feels particularly laboured in Gemini Rue. The rigmarole of having to tap on an elevator for a menu to press the button, then having to tap again to walk in, is exhausting.

■ Grungy colours convey the brooding atmosphere of this cyberpunk detective story

Fortunately, the game's plotline offers a significant enough pay off to make up for the hours of repetitive tapping. Set in a war-torn galaxy, the game switches between the stories of playable characters Azriel the detective, who is searching for his missing brother, and Delta Six, a patient in a mysterious space-station hospital who has

had his memory wiped. From the premise alone this storyline seems predictable, but a third-act twist makes for an explosive finale.

**A gripping plot and saxophone-laden track make Gemini Rue an great neo-noir, though the controls kill the mood.**

★★★★☆

● Price £2.99/$3.99

# Return to Castlerama

## Sequel to the game billed as a 'photo-realistic walk'

Adventure games, particularly the point-and-click variety, were incredibly popular in the '90s. The Nintendo DS, smartphones and tablets have since helped to revitalise the genre. As a result, Castlerama tried to tap into this market back in 2011 by allowing people to walk around a fantasy world. They have gone further with Return To Castlerama, creating a proper, more developed game.

You start with a cut-scene that shows a character called David entering a secret passageway, and as you walk around using intuitive controls you can pick up some scrolls and read them, slowly building up a story arc. However, while the revelations of David's destiny are enjoyable, this is not

Monkey Island or Broken Sword. The thing is, you soon realise that picking up these scrolls and wandering around is all you are doing. There are no puzzles to write home about and interactivity is rather sparse. There is a sense that you have to complete tasks and play out the game in the exact order that the developers want it to progress in. It's hard to see the point when the world you are exploring isn't all that exciting. In a genre that relies on good gameplay to motivate you, this is a disappointment.

**Adventure game fans will notice the lack of interactivity and puzzle-solving in a game where it should be key.**

★★☆☆☆

■ The graphics feel a little last-gen and don't draw you in a great deal

■ The characters and story arc try in vain to make this

● Price **Free**

# Diner Dash

## Get your skates on – people are getting hungry

 Working in a restaurant isn't always great fun but somehow Diner Dash makes it rather charming. With bold, colourful graphics to draw you in and a style that will make it a hit with younger gamers, this time management app will almost certainly keep you on your toes as you go from one table to the next, dealing with orders, conversing with chef and serving food, trying to do as many as you can in order to earn bonus points.

You get seven levels for free and then you have to start shelling out but those seven levels certainly provide lots of entertainment. You can unlock additional restaurants through in-app purchases but it becomes so addictive that you may not begrudge doing so. There is so much to deal with as you try to keep customers happy, ensure they pay

and try and figure out the best way to get maximum tips.

As you get better, you are able to progress more quickly up the ladder and leave the run-of-the-mill cafe behind as you go for more impressive surroundings and better class of customer. To help you on your way, there is a Dash Mart where you will find boosts and upgrades and this will give you some added pleasure.

Whether or not you enjoy Diner Dash may depend on your thoughts regarding in-app purchases but there is a lot of fun to be had here, and it deserves a chance.

**A game that will keep you on your toes as you try and keep all of your customers happy.**

★★★★☆

■ The game's all about keeping the customers happy and their tummys full while the clock keeps ticking, but watch out as they may be difficult

■ There is a wide selection of restaurants to choose from, including some exotic locations and situations once you've earned access to them

---

● Price **£3.99/$6.99**

# RE-VOLT Classic

## Just a little re-volting

 RE-VOLT Classic is based on a classic racer on the PlayStation. Normally this isn't worth pointing out, but when little has been done to overhaul the game to run on mobile devices that are considerably more powerful than the PS1, it seems like a shame.

Though there's a wide number of different tracks to race around, visually RE-VOLT Classic doesn't do much to bring them into the modern era. Controls-wise the mechanics have ported over well, though here you'll only control steering – which can be a bit of a pain when stuck

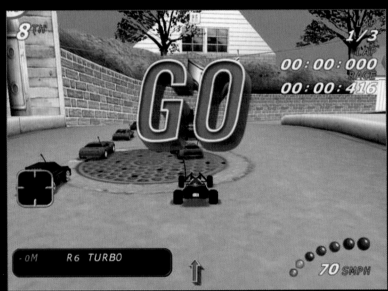
■ The arcade style retains some of the original PlayStation feel and simplicity

Mechanically the driving does feel fairly reminiscent of real-life remote-control car racing, but more often than not the vehicle will flip out of control for no reason – a major flaw when it's the key selling point.

RE-VOLT Classic is a fun experience,

modernise the game it's already behind the competition in practically every way.

**Fun enough to keep you occupied, but lacks the quality to compete with the best on the market.**

★★★☆☆

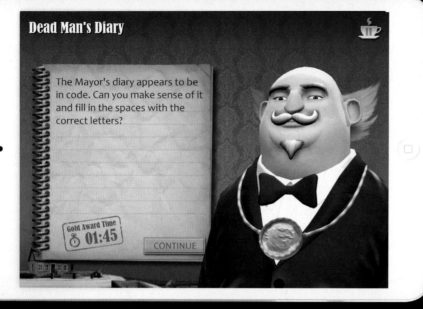

Dead Man's Diary

The Mayor's diary appears to be in code. Can you make sense of it and fill in the spaces with the correct letters?

Gold Award Time
01:45

CONTINUE

● Price £1.99/$2.99

# Murder Files
## Murder mystery for iOS

Board games like Cluedo are the last bastion of the classic murder mystery; that is until now. Murder Files is full of the melodrama, caricature characters and over-the-top humour, and

has been neatly fused here with a host of touch-screen mini games in order to create a fun gaming experience. The aim is to solve each puzzle and move forward in the game, gathering evidence and looking out

for clues in order to solve cases. With four episodes and each one taking roughly half an hour or more to complete, there is plenty of gaming time. The puzzles on offer will test your powers of deduction in many ways, whether it be maths, memory or logic, and given the light-hearted nature of the animation and the narration this is almost a surprise.

There is plenty to enjoy and be charmed by in Murder Files, but at times the cut scenes and story telling do dominate too much, and users can't help but feel that the it's is trying too hard to make fun of itself.

This is worth your time if you love a good old-fashioned murder mystery, but you must be prepared to give up a fair amount of it to succeed, though you will be rewarded by flashes of humour.

**Great if a fan of murder mysteries, but does try too hard in places to poke fun at itself.**

★★★★★

● Price £0.69/$0.99

# City Of Secrets 2: Episode 1
## What secrets can Moles the Mole find in Pocopane?

The classic adventure game genre has had a resurgence in recent years, and now console ports have found success too.

Brand new efforts like City of Secrets are also rising to the challenge. Its sequel, City of Secrets 2, sends you back down to the city of Pocopane as Moles the Mole is in search of ingredients for an unholy fettuccine dish.

The writing is witty and clever, with situations and conversations occasionally breaking the fourth-wall for some extra well-timed comedy. There is a fantastic array of logic and trading puzzles that are controlled through fairly simple and easy-to-understand touch controls.

If you're a bit stuck though, a handy tip mode highlights all the interactive objects, giving context-sensitive tips that offer just enough information to figure out what your next move should be.

These were always correctly presented in order, however if you like you can up the difficulty and turn them off completely.

This is a nicely designed app that will keep you interested with a fun and interesting narrative.

**A fun and quite witty adventure that unfortunately suffers from intrusive ads, and also feels a little short.**

★★★★★

■ You'll meet Moles the Mole and help him cook

■ The gameplay is fun and the writing witty, making this a game you won't want to end

■ With many worlds to explore, the visuals are amazing and very much of a console quality

■ The typical Star Wars style will bring back memories for any fan, creating a nostalgic experience

● Price £2.99/$4.99

# Star Wars: Knights of the Old Republic

## Gamers will see the light with this tenth anniversary game

### PROS/CONS

▲ A faithful port that seems to have dated very little

▲ The plot is immersive with amazing action

▼ Controls can be a bit of a burden

▼ Storage space may be an issue at 2GB

Ten years isn't a long time when you are dealing with galaxies but it is long enough for us mere humans to get a pang of nostalgia. This is a port of a ten-year-old game that was an incredible success on the Xbox and PC back in 2003. To mark the anniversary of the classic game, it has been released on the iPad.

It's amazing to see how well it comes across. The Xbox was a very powerful machine in its day and the amazing visuals on offer here with console gameplay just goes to show the immense capabilities of today's technology.

As a Star Wars game, you get to see the inevitable opening sequence but it is the game itself that is the true star, not the peripheral bits around it. Although you can't run this on the iPad 1, the later iPads are more than up to the job as long as you have the storage space. Your reward is an RPG packed with lightsaber battles spread over eight enormous worlds, with a host of characters to interact with.

All of this is set 4,000 years before Anakin Skywalker's arrival so don't expect many familiar here – not that it makes a difference. The pace of the game and the plot with its engaging narrative keeps the whole thing moving along.

In addition to mastering the Force, you choose how your character develops by selecting how they respond to questions. These actions determines whether your character will remain loyal to the Jedi or become a villainous Sith Lord.

Controls can be fiddly at times and they take a bit of getting used to, but you'll soon adjust to them and get immersed in the experience. For the price, you are getting an incredible bargain with a great amount of longevity.

**An undoubted classic with plenty of variety that will never go to the dark side of your iPad. The visuals and gameplay translate well to the iPad.**

★★★★★

## "An RPG packed with lightsaber battles spread over eight enormous worlds, with a host of characters"

■ You can customise your entire character, from gender to outfit

● Price £4.99/$6.99

# Frozen Synapse

## A modernisation of the classic tactical strategy game

Frozen Synapse is a remarkably detailed strategy game that puts you in command of a small team of armed insurgents who have to neutralise the enemy. You have to physically plot every step of your team's assault through the buildings and then indicate the point at which they are to engage the enemy. The twist is that each wave of moves must fit within a five-second time frame – so you can either use the time to move each ally into position and take out each enemy one-on-one or use it to unite your team and have them flank enemies individually to minimise casualties.

You can try as many tactics as you want, discovering how best to utilise the time and your surroundings. However, once you press the 'Prime' button, your move becomes active and you must watch how your plans

translate to the real-time battlefield. This is when the game comes alive because you realise that your enemies aren't just mindless drones fixed to one spot, they are living people and will do anything to evade danger.

This is what makes the game so compelling, because you can either gleefully see your best laid plans coming to fruition – or watch as everything falls apart and you start losing men. If the price of the game doesn't hint that it is no throwaway title, then the volume of tutorial videos slams the fact home. There is much to learn, not least the assignment of commands and plotting a waypoint route through the terrain from your command centre.

The only downer comes in the touchscreen interface as vital details can be missed as your finger obscures them, but this is a minor aside in an otherwise enjoyable and immersive experience.

**A deeply engrossing, thought-evoking and intelligent tactical strategy game. It might seem pricey, but this only reflects its quality.**

★ ★ ★ ★ ★

> "There is much to learn, not least the assignment of commands to your troops"

■ There is a campaign map ready to assault with various story elements

■ As the amount of tactics in the game suggests, there's a lot to master to play it successfully

■ How the opposition will react is completely out of your hands

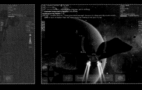

● Price £1.49/$1.99

# The Other Brothers

 Sure, another retro platformer may not sound wholly original, but subtle differences set The Other apart from the crowd. While simplistic, the quirky graphics work well to create an engaging atmosphere. The gameplay is even better: in fact, we reckon this is one of the best 2D platformers currently available. Plus, considering the low price, this one is well worth downloading for hours of fun.

**A great twist on retro gaming, with modern advances built in.**

★★★★★

● Price £0.69/$0.99

# Vendetta Online

 The desirability of a game which is a well-known franchise is hard to ignore. In terms of squeezing a console-quality title onto a tablet, this game does well, but there is still a sense that the ambition gets in the way of the gaming experience. The stunning graphics are rightfully promoted as a highlight, but an awful lot is going on at a time and the end result is a slightly crowded experience that feels overly complex a lot of the time.

**An ambitious game that might be too complex for the mobile tablet form.**

★★★★★

● Price £1.49/$1.95

# They Need To Be Fed 2

 Cute meets complex in this unusual platformer that'll test you to the extreme. Standard aspects include collecting objects and completing levels, but it is the 360° gravitational forces that make it feel unusual as you progress through increasing areas of difficulty. Add in some cute graphics, which don't quite fit with its complex nature, and the game comes together nicely. Similar games are available, but this is one of the best.

**A tricky platformer joining physics and cute graphics for a decent experience.**

★★★★★

● Price Free

# CSR Racing

 CSR Racing lets you take part in various drag races and time your boosts to perfection, and you can increase the performance of your cars by winning, creating a sense of achievement the whole way through. Add some extremely pleasing graphics and we have a winner. The only potential downside is that the longevity may not be enough if you want more variety.

**A beautiful-looking racer with enough features to keep you interested.**

★★★★★

● Price Free

# Dungeon Hunter 4

 When a game is so highly anticipated, it is hard for it to live up to expectations, but this one really does. The graphics are incredibly detailed, even though there is a lot going on, and the way it has been programmed also means that it runs smoothly. This game really feels like a console title shrunk down for the iPad and it's hard to criticise. You could spend hours immersed in this title without noticing.

**A sensational game that'll keep you hooked for hours on end.**

★★★★★

● Price £2.49/$3.99

# The Thirty-Nine Steps

 You could be forgiven for thinking that this is just a retelling of the classic John Buchan novel, but there's a lot more here. Some of the animations and graphics are breathtaking and it shows what is possible if a lot of care goes into how the interface fits with the story. The experience can become addictive as you unlock achievements, but it never feels like a game based on a story.

**A game/book that pushes the boundaries of digital storytelling.**

★★★★★

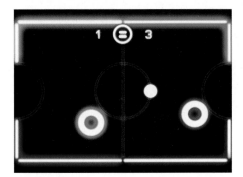

● Price £2.99/$3.99

# Backgammon NJ

● Price £0.69/$0.99

# Slingshot Racing

● Price £0.69/$0.99

# Glow Hockey 2

 This game is based on airhockey, where the aim is to hit the puck into the opponent's goal with a paddle, and works just like the real thing. In fact, the only thing it doesn't seem to replicate is the din created by two people repeatedly smashing plastic together – but you can probably live without that.

**Takes a game suited for touchscreen and turns it into a same-screen gem.**
★★★★★

 Board games are a natural fit for same-screen apps, and backgammon is nicely reproduced in this simulation. In a two-player game you take it in turns to roll the virtual dice by tapping on the screen and then choose where to put your checkers. There are a host of settings you can play with, including options to change the appearance and adjust the skill level. There are also helpful instructions if you're new to the game.

**Not a party game but a perfect fit for a family tournament.**
★★★★★

 Imagine the pod race from Star Wars: Episode I done steampunk-style and you've got Slingshot Racing. You race a go kart around a variety of tracks but the only control you have is around the corners, which is determined by whether you activate a slingshot at the right time. Hit it too early and you crash into the wall; too late and you run off the edge. The designs range from simple to infuriating, and there are many options to sustain interest.

**Regardless of where you finish, this game will be a winner anywhere.**
★★★★★

● Price Free

# Fast & Furious 6: The Game

● Price £1.49/$1.99

# The Room

 We have not seen a mobile game as atmospheric and focused as The Room. It requires logic and deep thought, and you need to think about the objects available and how to use them to solve the next part of the puzzle. Some parts take minutes and others a day or two, but the rewards are worth it in this strange and wonderful, engrossing world.

**A hugely atmospheric puzzler that'll keep you engrossed for ages.**
★★★★★

● Price £0.69/$0.99

# Slayin

 There are elements within Slayin that make it an excellent platform game. It doesn't look very original due to the retro graphics, but in terms of pure gameplay it's a winner, though the endless experience means this game is definitely one for the hardened gamer, despite many positive aspects. Brilliant, but with potentially limited appeal.

**A brilliant platforming game which will appeal most to experienced gamers.**
★★★★★

 The Fast & Furious series has been updated yet again. Gradually build up your rides and take on a variety of opponents who are faster, more powerful and, at times, feel impossible to beat. The simplistic nature of drag racing and the lack of controls work well with the ultra-realistic graphics. Longevity is also assured thanks to the progressive nature of the challenges. Hard to put down.

**Drag racing clothed in realistic 3D graphics and a genuine sense of speed.**
★★★★★

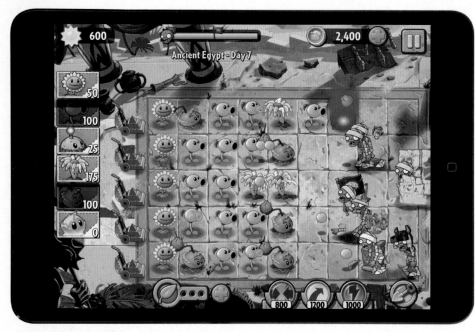

■ Smart tactics and strategy will help you progress through the game

■ There are three main historical settings to fight your way through

● Price **Free**

# Plants vs Zombies 2

## The battle for garden supremacy spills across time

### PROS/CONS
▲ Takes the best aspects of the original and expands on them

▲ New worlds bring some much-needed upscaling to the game

▼ The in-app purchasing structure blocks some plants from use

▼ The difficulty level is no match for buying a few upgrades

It might sound the most unlikely of rivalries, but the battle in the backyard between plants and zombies has captured the imagination, and has now finally returned for a much-anticipated sequel.

This time around things are a little different, with so much more scale to the game – rather than taking place around your virtual 'home' you take off on an adventure through time along with Crazy Dave and his talking camper van. There is an almost board game format to the game's layout, with levels needing to be completed before you can move forward in a world. Speaking of worlds, there are three iconic time periods to do battle in, starting in Ancient Egypt, before

moving to the 18th Century and the pirate-laden high seas and finally finishing in the Wild West.

Of course it's not as simple as just passing each level and moving on to the next, Plants vs Zombies 2 asks you to gather stars in order to unlock the gates that lead to new worlds. In order to get stars players have to go back and repeat completed levels, meeting gradually more difficult objectives to work your way up to the maximum three stars per level.

As well as this, players can look out for keys that unlock alternative paths on your route through the game. These lead to bonus levels with specific parameters; ranging from a certain set of plants to use, to producing a set amount of sun and beyond, and

stars are also on offer here. Suddenly this universe feels a whole lot bigger and that is a very good thing. This sequel feels more engaging than the original, and with zombies unique to each world there is far more variety to your enemy than previously, instantly making for a more exciting experience. Look out for zombies protected by Egyptian tombs, undead swashbucklers and Stetson wearers across the different settings, as well as some cool traits like certain Egyptian zombies being able to lure away your sun. Also be keep an eye out for the 'endless' levels that appear at the end of each world, where players can try and survive level after level, carrying resources through each battle, and any lawnmowers that survive. It's another dimension to the game, and provides a break from the traditional structure that players are used to.

It's pretty clear that a lot of effort has been made to ensure that this sequel offers more, and that all the

## "This sequel feels more engaging than the original, and with zombies unique to each world there is far more variety"

■ As well as the main story, there are side missions to earn you upgrades and coins

anticipation around it will be backed up. The original Plants vs Zombies was and remains one of the shining examples of what makes mobile gaming great – a simple setup and objectives, engaging visuals and that flurry of screen tapping that is inevitable when a game has completely grabbed you.

On the subject of screen interactivity, it's worth highlighting another interesting aspect of the gameplay that has been tweaked for Plants vs Zombies 2; players can now, if they have the in-game coins to afford it, jump in and use their own fingers to take out zombies for themselves. There are three new power-up options that allow players to use gestures to soften up incoming waves. Combine these with the Plant Food upgrades that give

individual plants epic attacks, and this suddenly feels a lot less tower defence and more offence.

The only sticking point for certain users will be the in-app purchases, a mobile gaming structure that continues to gripe with some. The bottom line in relation to Plants vs Zombies 2 is that it's more than possible to be able to play through the whole game without having to ever visit the store. Fans of the series will be disappointed to see some old favourites behind the paywall, but the new added dimensions within this sequel help to soften this blow for gamers significantly.

There is the argument that playing through without turning to real money is the better option anyway. With infinite power-ups and plant food, even the most intense zombie wave can be swotted away, and that misses the point of what Plants vs Zombies is all about. This is a fantastic game that will engage gamers for hours on end.

**It's taken time to arrive, but this has made step-ups in the right places and takes the app forward.**

■ The types of plants available through in-app purchases have also been expanded

# Showcase
## The elements of great sequel

### 01: Worlds
This time around the battle has moved beyond the backyard and instead sees players venture back in time to Ancient Egypt, the high seas and the Wild West.

### 02: Zombies
To perfectly match each of these new worlds, your attackers have now gone native too, so be on the lookout for zombie pharaohs, pirates, cowboys and many more.

### 03: Plant food
A very cool and explosive upgrade that allows you to give a single plant a dose of plant food, with some pretty devastating results for your oncoming enemy.

### 04: Power-ups
For the first time you can enter the action yourself, using gesture controls to take out some of the oncoming undead. It offers more variety in some fantastic gameplay.

### 05: Challenges
Beside the main story levels, look out for extra challenges along the way. These can help you earn valuable coins, stars and keys to further your progress in the overall game.

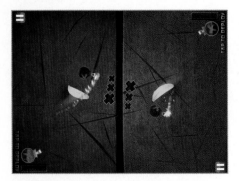

## Games

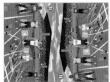

**Price £0.69/$0.99**

# Summer Games 3D

 In this app you represent a country in athletics, cycling, rowing or swimming events, competing against virtual rivals or friends. The gameplay is good fun thanks to the simple and effective touchscreen controls. Simultaneous same-screen play can be used for events in which participants compete at the same time, such as running. Other events require that you take it in turns. Thanks to the variable difficulty, it should be challenging enough to keep you interested.

**Gives your fingers a workout while the rest doesn't break a sweat. Great fun.**

★★★★☆

**Price £0.99/$1.49**

# Bridgy Jones™

 There have been many attempts at bridge-building games, but few are as graphically impressive as Bridgy Jones. The early levels look and feel good, but as the complexity increases the interface is tricky and gets in the way of the gameplay. It's a potentially fun experience, but the controls and touch interface need adjusting.

**Potentially an absorbing experience, but it's a little too fiddly to play.**

★★★☆☆

**Price £0.69/$0.99**

# Fruit Ninja

 Fruit Ninja is one of the most addictive games to exploit the touchscreen. Different kinds of fruit shoot up and you swipe across to chop them up, but be sharp to avoid striking the bombs. Two multiplayer modes are available on tablets: Classic Attack (play until you run out of lives or you hit a bomb) and Zen Duel (a timed duel).

**The ultimate in fast and furious fruity fun. Bound to be a hit amongst friends.**

★★★★★

**Price Free**

# Stick Cricket Partnerships

 This game makes no attempt to present a realistic cricket experience, but it does manage to offer fun and easy gameplay. Having said that, it is difficult to win every time and it will keep you coming back, but there are some areas that need adjustment. The in-app purchasing is a little on the aggressive side, which may put you off, and the online feature isn't as reliable as it should be.

**A fun experience, but requires in-app purchasing to be enjoyed fully.**

★★★☆☆

**Price £1.49/$1.99**

# Super Mega Worm

 Describing Super Mega Worm is not easy. Your task is to eat as many people and creatures as possible by ascending from below the earth and gobbling them up. Yes, really. It's a crazy premise, but thanks to the retro graphics it never feels overly violent and the controls make it quite addictive as you complete combos. Overall, it offers all the elements to keep you entertained.

**Violence, cuteness and bonkers gameplay all in retro graphics. Brilliant!**

★★★★☆

**Price £0.69/$0.99**

# Beach Games

 Beach Games is a curious app. On the one hand you are given a series of fun mini-games, but each of these requires a lot of practice and near-perfect timing. On the other hand, some may find it all too simplistic. It certainly has charm and acts as a fun diversion, but it needs additional content to make it truly enjoyable.

**A game that some will love and others will hate. It's still worth a try, however.**

★★★☆☆

■ The different areas of space really add to the feeling of exploration

■ The look of the game is reminiscent of Pixel People or Habbo Hotel, as is its gameplay

● Price £1.99/$2.99

# Star Command
## Take control of your universe

**PROS/CONS**

▲ Perfectly taps into sci-fi geekdom, handing you your own spaceship

▲ A fantastic-looking game from every single angle

▼ The difficulty curve is rather alarmingly steep

▼ The precise controls don't favour iPhone use

This game gives users the chance to take command of their own deep-space explorer. You fly your ship, and control the crew, weapons and shields. In iOS gaming terms Star Command feels like a distant relative of games like Pixel People and The Sims, where the little universe you create is entirely in your control, with taps and swipes in order to move those that inhabit it between their various jobs. Here, you must fill your ship with crew by spending tokens to employ them. There are three main types of crew member: engineer, weapons expert and medical staff, and assigning them to a certain room on your ship pigeonholes them in that career, as well as colour-codes them. There's even a Star Trek in-joke in your weapons and security crew members – those first in danger, being in red.

It takes a few minutes to find your bearings and understand the basic jobs of your crew, but there's then a startling pace to the game that thoroughly tests the knowledge you've managed to scoop up so far.

On just your second mission you're asked to deal with 'invaders' teleporting onto your ship, where you scramble to get your red-shirted security team to fight off various

species. All the while moving engineers to repair damage your ship has sustained, and your medical staff to heal injured crew. It's fast-paced and difficult; most levels taking at least one attempt to survive and complete, but you do want to keep trying; that's the frustrating beauty of it.

There is romance in commanding your own ship, and in a game that's been so lovingly put together, this isn't a temptation you should resist.

**It might be a challenge to complete but you'll keep coming back. Besides, who wouldn't want to control their own spaceship?**

★★★★★

■ There are plenty of other ships battle with across the galaxy

"There's a startling pace to the game that thoroughly tests the knowledge you've scooped up"

 **Games**

● Price £4.99/$6.99

# Grand Theft Auto: San Andreas

**One of gaming's best franchises fires on to iOS**

 While Grand Theft Auto V attracts praise on consoles and is considered one of the best games of all time, seeing one of its predecessors, San Andreas, arrive on tablet is no less of a thrill. Considering how influential this game was at the time, to have a flagship console game on mobile shows just how far smart devices have come.

San Andreas was originally released in 2004 and, since that time, millions of people will have enjoyed playing as CJ, who has returned home to the city of Los Santos following the murder of his mother.

The storyline urges the player to re-establish CJ's old gang, fight corrupt cops, and solve his mother's murder. There's enough conflict and intrigue to keep the player interested, that's for sure. The graphics have been given a HD polish

with advanced lighting so this 10-year-old game looks more last-gen rather than previous-to-last-gen. The story itself remains the same – with the swearing, adult content, car jacking and Hollywood violence – but the controls have been reinvented. Things are more fiddly than on a control pad and, while there are different options for controlling vehicles, none of them are truly intuitive.

We kept finding vehicles careering off to one side - though, of course, this could have been due to how we were playing rather than the game's responsiveness. However, the controls react to the gameplay so that they don't overcrowd the screen; for example, when you get close to a vehicle, a button to hijack cars will temporarily appear. Elsewhere, the missions remain challenging but now have checkpoints, making messing up during set pieces less frustrating. Overall, a great game with hours of replay value.

**A modern classic which kept its look while being updated for handheld devices. Though the controls aren't perfect, it's a valiant effort.**

★★★★☆

> **"The graphics have been given a HD polish so this 10-year-old game looks more last-gen"**

■ San Andreas was the first GTA game to add rural areas to the franchise's already massive map

■ If you find your car is out of control, it can lead to some impressive stunts

■ One of the most familiar scenes in GTA is car-jacking, where you can steal any vehicle

■ This game marks yet another step forward in terms of the graphic quality on mobile devices

■ Gesture-heavy combat is the main focus of this large-scale game

● Price £4.99/$6.99

# Infinity Blade III
## The mobile hack-n-slash heavyweight concludes its trilogy

### PROS/CONS

▲ Visually, it's a wonderful world to explore

▲ A second playable character and new features freshen things up

▼ Nothing hugely revolutionary in the gameplay

▼ The repetition and difficulty curve can drag at times

It's taken some time to surface, but the third instalment of the Infinity Blade series has finally arrived on iPhone and iPad.

Much like the previous titles, this game sticks to what it knows best in terms of the gameplay, keeping repetitive slash-heavy battles at its core. What you will notice is how much bigger the game is, and how much better it looks. Things are much more polished this time, and considering Infinity Blade has never been a bad-looking game, it means things really do look gorgeous now.

The world you play in is also on a much bigger scale, and though there is less of the path choice and exploration that we found in Infinity Blade II, there is a suitable impression of size and general epicness that developers Chair seem quite keen to get across.

In terms of gameplay things are very much familiar, with the same gesture-laden combat the focal point of your gaming. A few layers have been added to and around this though; users can now add a finishing move to their combos thanks to an on-screen swipe prompt. It's a great way to do some extra damage.

The new achievement system also rewards players for varying up how they fight, with valuable chips on offer for hitting certain numbers of parries, dodges and blocks, so it pays to mix things up a bit. Isa is a playable character for the first time too, and you can level her up independently to Siris. There's also a blacksmith and potions master to

work with in this game, and while some of their processes can take a fair chunk of time, there are many rewards in using them.

Rather than a massive overhaul this is very much a polished continuation of the story. Some of the narrative will be lost on you if you haven't played the previous games, but don't let that stop you from playing what is a benchmark in iOS gaming.

**This new addition adds some layers to the gameplay that fans of the previous titles should really appreciate.**

★★★★★

■ There are enemies of all shapes and sizes to engage in battle

■ Players can choose how to approach conversations, and each action has a consequence

■ Your screen can become filled with buttons, which can become overwhelming at times

● Price £4.99/$6.99

# Deus Ex: The Fall

## A big-name console title trying to bring it all to iOS

For some time now, games have been trying to close the gap on their console cousins in terms of looks and gameplay – no mean feat it's fair to say. Still, there has been some success in the tribute-style games like Modern Combat, which takes its inspiration from Call Of Duty and has gotten progressively better with each instalment.

The developers at Square Enix have decided to push one of their famed console titles onto the mobile platform in quite a big way – not with a port or homage to Deus Ex, but with an original game. Deus Ex: The Fall is set within the same universe as the three previous console titles, but in a different part, with its own characters and story. For die-hard fans of the

series this story takes place after the events of the tie-in novel, The Icarus Effect, in the year 2027.

Everything about this game sticks true to the console origins of the franchise, and you might be forgiven for thinking that your device is trying to install a fully-fledged gaming title given the amount of space needed (1.6GB). Having said that, a few seconds into the opening cut-scene and you will begin to understand just what all that space is being used for, because make no mistake, The Fall is a fantastic-looking mobile game. The golden tint to the world that we saw in the most recent console game, Human Revolution, has been transported here with some stunning lighting effects throughout the various environments.

On the subject of environment, the Deus Ex open-world experience is here too, with items and objects to help you along the way, and with every action having a consequence. On this level, The Fall is one of the deepest games on iOS in terms of just about everything. There is a massive array of weapons and items to purchase and upgrade to, and then there is the huge augmentation aspect that forms such a central part of the Deus Ex gameplay – the upgrades to your abilities that enable players to complete missions. These themselves take you from mafia hideouts in Moscow to slums in Panama and beyond.

The biggest challenge for this game was, as is always the case when it comes to shooters on mobile, how the controls are translated to the touchscreen. In terms of movement things are quite elegant with invisible controls; the left side of the screen deals with your actual movement, while the right controls your field of

## "The Fall is set within the same universe as the three previous console titles, but in a different part, with its own characters and story"

■ Users have the option to take out enemies using stealth or brute force

vision, as is traditional with first-person shooters. There is also the option to double tap somewhere and move to that point, a nice alternative to aid your movement in the game.

Things take a less positive turn when it comes to the more frenetic gameplay – for example, when you find yourself in a close-quarters firefight, something that can be a regular occurrence. The issue is the number of buttons on-screen to some extent, where if you get flanked by an enemy you'll need to tap the exit cover button, locate your target and then tap fire, all of which will take a couple of seconds. This is enough time to see you take some hits and get frustrated. It is at this point that the screen feels too full and busy for the first time. Square Enix has worked hard to make everything you need in Deus

Ex accessible, and any veterans of the series will tell you this is a fair amount. But in trying to do so, things become cluttered and at times chaotic as you search for the controls.

However, an interesting development of the game's migration to the touchscreen has been the improved functionality of the hacking mini-game when trying to open doors. Being able to simply tap each node to complete the hack is a much smoother process than on controller – a very happy discovery.

There is no doubting the fantastic looks and depth to The Fall, and this is definitely another step forward for mobile gaming. The statement of making this an original title, not streamlined, adds to the idea that iOS and Android could one day rival consoles. But Deus Ex has been unable to solve the issue that mobile shooters have always had, and that is a smooth mix of pointing and shooting. This is progress, but not quite the epiphany.

**An enjoyable instalment that takes mobile gaming forward, though it hasn't conquered it.**

 ★★★★☆

■ The epic style and incredible depth make this a significant step in mobile gaming

## Showcase
### Best parts of The Fall

**01: The visuals**
There is no doubting just how good this game looks, with stunning lighting effects and expansive environments that are very impressive for a mobile game.

**02: Open world**
Much like the console versions, there are open world aspects to Deus Ex, with big areas to explore and more than one route on offer with everything you do, so you can move freely.

**03: The story**
Square Enix and Eidos decided to use the same writers and voice actors as they did for the console games, so The Fall has the depth to match its great looks, and will satisfy fans.

**04: The weapons**
You will struggle to find a game that has the sheer mass of weapons and tweaks to match this one. It's an impressive haul of machinery that leaves you plenty of options.

**05: Augmentation**
At the centre of Deus Ex is human augmentation. This physical upgrade system is on full display here, with as much diversity as the previous games.

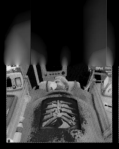

● Price £2.99/$4.99

# Carp Fishing Simulator

 Fishing is not the ideal game for any computing device, but the sheer amount of realism and graphical polish on show in Carp Fishing Simulator is very impressive. It will help if you already enjoy fishing because patience is required, but over time we found the experience quite compelling and well worth the effort. Certainly an intriguing mobile fishing game, but maybe only for a niche audience.

**This game is the nearest we have seen to real fishing on a phone or tablet.**

★★★★★

● Price £1.99/$2.99

# Construction Simulator 2014

 There are some games that should logically sit on consoles and desktop computers and this is one of them. Nevertheless, the developer has somehow managed to make it perfectly playable on the smaller screen and given us a raft of construction features to play with. Everything on offer here, from the slick graphics and controls to the long-term playability, is up there with the very best. Brilliant.

**A highly ambitious game that pulls it all off with aplomb.**

★★★★★

● Price £2.49/$5.99

# Surgeon Simulator

 Would you really want to be a surgeon? The pressure of dealing with complex tools and the knowledge that one wrong move could end a life is a lot to handle, but this game somehow manages to encapsulate those emotions. There is blood flying everywhere, a pressurising timer and fiddly controls that make it all the more absorbing as you attempt to complete each quest.

**An original game that will leave you feeling energised.**

★★★★★

● Price £0.69/$2.99

# Rollercoaster Tycoon 4

## Unleash your inner theme park designer

 RollerCoaster Tycoon, like Transport Tycoon before it, is one of those titles that has a lot of goodwill associated with it for its various PC versions. This mobile incarnation brings the basics of the game to touchscreen devices, but something of the subtlety and charm of the original is lost along the way. The graphics are cartoony and appealing, and there is a lot of fun in planning out your own theme park – not to mention designing your own rollercoasters – but the game is let down significantly in certain areas.

Of course a game has to lose some of its depth when it makes the switch to a smaller screen and a more basic interface, but RollerCoaster Tycoon 4 Mobile comes across as a bit too simplistic. Whether it's

the restrictions on how you can build your rollercoasters, or the easy prompts about what to do next, there's not much depth here. You do get a large chunk of money and tickets to get started with (both used as currency within the game), but after a couple of hours you'll need to shell out cold hard cash or wait eons (in mobile gaming years) for anything to be built. It's certainly a bright diversion that will fill up some minutes of your spare time, but serious gamers, particularly fans, will come away feeling disappointed.

**Provides a couple of hours of gaming fun, but there's really not much depth or long-term appeal here.**

★★★☆☆

■ Build your park according to your own vision

■ The classic computer game has finally made its way onto mobile

● Price **Free**

# Clash of Clans

## Develop your village or go to war!

Despite being one of the most popular games on mobile, Clash Of Clans was a rather run-of-the-mill free-to-play strategic action game until its recent update. You develop your fledging village into a masterful dominion by ransacking other player's bases for gold so that you can build bigger and better weapons and level up. However, the game was given its biggest update ever in April, adding a new feature: Clan Wars. Now up to 100 players (50 versus 50) can choose to duke it out in an epic battle on a massive war map, working together as clans to attack enemy bases to earn the most gold stars.

When the battle ends, the clan with the most gold stars wins and the spoils of war are divided between the winning clan members. The war games are so large that they take two days to play, with a day of preparation before the onslaught even begins.

The game does feature some in-app purchases in order to progress in the game, similar to other strategy games, and this can cause some frustration. If you're a patient gamer, though, you can progress the old fashioned way.

**Starting an epic war with so many other players is a great feature, but prepared to work hard for your gold.**

★★★★☆

● Price **£4.99/$6.99**

# Pandemic: The Board Game

## Save the world from infectious diseases

Designed for two to four players, Pandemic (a faithful reproduction of the board game) is unlike other games in that you work co-operatively as a team to beat the game, rather than compete to beat other players. This means that it works as a single-player game too, with you taking the other players' turns.

The game is played on a world map on which the major cities are highlighted. There are four virulent diseases infecting certain cities and you are part of a team of people trying to eradicate the contagions. Each member has different abilities and four actions can be taken per turn. They could travel to a city, cure the infection there, and so on. Cards are dealt on each turn and collecting the right ones enables a cure to be found for a disease. The aim is to cure all four of the diseases.

If you have played the board game you'll be right at home with the iPad app in no time at all, but newcomers could struggle with the complex rules. With a multi-page manual that is essential reading, the first hour isn't much fun. Don't give up, this is a great game that will keep you engaged.

**This multiplayer board game works as well in single-player mode as it does in multiplayer, and is very entertaining.**

★★★★☆

■ A team member can perform four actions per turn

■ Each member has different abilities and this affects the gameplay

 Games

● Price **Freemium**

# Real Racing 3

## Start your engines... ready...set...go!

 Race your friends in Real Racing 3 – even when they are offline. The game's so-called Time-Shifted Multiplayer means that you are never playing a fake computer opponent, as every racer is a ghost of another player's best time, but with improved AI, which is a very clever addition to what would otherwise be a standard racing game. The game will randomly assign ghosts of other racers to chase, or if you have connected with friends via Facebook or Game Center, it will automatically pit you against them instead. This is ideal for casual mobile gaming – or when you may fancy a race to pass the time but your friends are

inconveniently unavailable. However, as impressive as this technology is, it doesn't compare to the thrill of going bumper to bumper in real-time multiplayer.

Unfortunately, Real Racing 3 is limited to only four players, which is half as many as previous Real Racing games have supported. Still, the game makes up for this with hyper-realistic graphics that render real-world cars

and tracks beautifully, only to show physical car damage as you smash into an opponent. New cars and locations are also updated quite regularly.

---

**A fun racing game that handles beautifully and looks good too. A shame it can't support more players.**

★★★★☆

● Price Free

# Golf Star™

## Looks so good you can almost read the greens

 Sometimes you can be sold just by looking at a game, and Golf Star™ is one of these occasions. There's an arcade feel to this game as users must perform over a series of tutorial holes to begin levelling up, which will eventually unlock additional gameplay modes, mainly focused on multiplayer. There's a reward system involved as players constantly earn coins for good shots, and XP with each round that's completed. This goes towards levelling up, and indeed opening more aspects of the game, providing an incentive to keep playing.

The visuals remain the real star of this game, and are very impressive, especially considering that this game is free to download. The smoothness and simple

control system make for an enticing pick-up-and-play title. It probably won't take over your gaming life, but you'll enjoy dipping in and out of it. This is where the multiplayer and one-on-one match modes are handy.

The in-app purchases come into play a little earlier than we would like, but this is quite literally a price worth paying considering the level of visual quality you're getting for nothing in the first place. Don't look a gift horse in the mouth, we would say.

---

**A very easy to pick up and put down game that looks absolutely great: a bit of a hidden gem.**

★★★★★

■ The control system is easy to get to grips with, revolving around a power gauge

■ The quality of design is a real plus for this surprisingly addictive sports game

● Price £1.49/$1.99

# Solar Flux HD

## Collect plasma in your spaceship and fix failing stars

Solar Flux HD is an impressive physics-style game in which objects move in a semi-realistic way. The game takes place in outer space and the story is that the stars are dying. You control a small spaceship and must collect plasma balls, firing them into the stars in order to regenerate them.

Your ship moves a bit like the one from the classic Asteroids game and you can fire your rocket in any direction. It takes time to accelerate, decelerate and change direction because of the ship's momentum. Plasma balls are scattered around the screen and you run in to them to collect them. Tap a star and the plasma ball is ejected into it.

It sounds simple, but it's not. On one level for example, you fly through an asteroid field picking up plasma balls

until you reach a planet. The planet's gravity pulls you into orbit and ejecting the plasma into the nearby star causes a wave. This knocks you out of orbit through a narrow gap in another asteroid belt where there are more plasma balls. Just as NASA uses the gravity of planets and moons to slingshot spacecrafts out into the solar system, you use them in the same way. Some plasma balls are close to stars and your shields start to burn away, so you can't afford to go slowly or the ship blows up.

As with other physics games, there are numerous levels to complete and they are very cleverly designed. They seem impossible at first, but they can be mastered with the right technique. This is an entertaining game with great graphics and fiendishly difficult puzzles. If you are looking for a new challenge, and like a bit of astronomy, then give this a try.

> "The games seem impossible at first, but they can be mastered with the right technique"

**If you like physics-based puzzle games you will love this space-themed one. It gets very addictive, very quickly.**

★★★★☆

COLLECT THE PLASMA

80%

RIDE FLARES TO CONSERVE FUEL.
COLLECT ALL PLASMA WITHOUT THRUSTING.

100

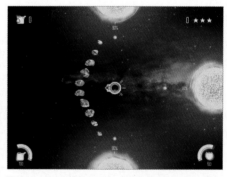

■ Three stars and asteroids complicate matters. If you're too close, your shields can burn

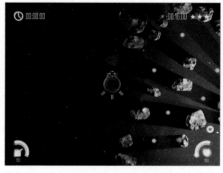

■ Flying through the universe becomes a beautiful, hypnotising experience

■ There are lots of asteroids in this galaxy and they are hard to avoid – it just takes practise

● Price £1.49/$1.99

# Simon The Sorcerer

 This is a classic game that started back in 1993, but it still holds up today in terms of how deep and addictive it is. The graphics certainly feel retro; while this complicates the control mechanisms in some areas, the charm has remained and any fan will enjoy it immensely. Unfortunately we experienced a few bugs and crashes, but hopefully these can be fixed in the future. Until then, it's still a great bit of gaming history.

**20 years since the original, it's back – but with a few bugs in tow.**

★★★★★

● Price Free

# Middle Manager Of Justice

 This interactive game falls between The Avengers and a fantasy football league. You train your team to fight crime, which is enjoyable, and with some skill the entire experience can be free. You need to remember, however, that in-app purchases may be needed from time to time. Still, the game keeps you amused for quite a while.

**A fun and colourful game that could have you hooked right from the start.**

★★★★★

● Price Free

# Le Vamp

 Despite including many features that have long been staples of platform games, the way Le Vamp is presented and the implementation of every element makes it feel like a console – and this alone kept us coming back for 'just one more go'. If you like running games, this one will appeal to you.

**A cute and engaging platform game that'll keep you coming back for more.**

★★★★★

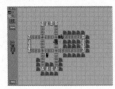
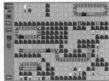

● Price £1.49/$1.99

# Ragtime Ruffian

 Ragtime Ruffian looks like a children's game, but after playing it you realise that the simplistic yet charming graphics actually add a lot to the experience, as do the sound effects and tunes. However, it is the puzzles that are the essential element here – they will keep you coming back, making your brain churn over. The endless mode is also great fun and the icing on the cake of this addictive game.

**A charming game with puzzles that will keep you thinking for ages.**

 ★★★★★

● Price £0.69/$1.29

# Men's Room Mayhem

 What can we say about Men's Room Mayhem? Think of the classic Flight Control but instead of planes you have men visiting the toilet. You have to ensure that they clean their hands and leave quickly without crossing the path of another. If they cross, a fight will ensue and you will have blood to clean up – indeed, cleanliness is important and required to progress. It has an bizarre, unusual theme, but it's good fun.

**An original take on a classic mobile game that's addictive and funny.**

 ★★★★☆

● Price £2.99/$4.99

# Leisure Suit Larry: Reloaded

 How can you improve on a classic like Leisure Suit Larry? It seems that updating graphics is not enough because in this game every part has been tweaked to make it feel like a title from 2013. Crucially, the story has stayed the same but everything else, from the animations to the jokes, has been improved and brought into the modern world. It feels like the classic, yet also brand new, which is a clever trick indeed.

**A classic reborn and it works on every single level. Fun all the way.**

 ★★★★★

● Price **Freemium**

# Fail Hard

Fail Hard looks similar to other bike-based games, but more polished. Traditional bike controls are used, but you get to play in different ways – although at times it can be very difficult understand what you need to do. More instructions would be useful, as would a slightly improved control mechanism.

**A beautifully presented biking game, but the controls could be improved.**

★★★☆☆

● Price **Freemium**

# World Of Cheese HD

This game looks like it has been designed for children thanks to the cute characters and colourful graphics, but when you start the first level and begin to scratch your head immediately, realisation dawns. This deceptively simple-looking game gets more complicated as it asks you to find hidden cheese in each location, and it's very easy to get immersed. This is a surprisingly intriguing and puzzling game for adults as well as children.

**A challenging puzzle game that will definitely tax your brain.**

★★★★☆

● Price **Free**

# Champ Man

Champ Man attempts to offer realism to the football management game format by using real data to aid familiarity. With more than 400 clubs, 21 leagues and a huge database of real players this game will soon start sucking up your time. The graphics aren't superb, but it isn't a huge problem.

**Football fanatics will love the detail and the realism. It is also very addictive.**

★★★★☆

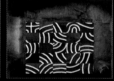

● Price **£0.69/$0.99**

# The Owlman of Mawnan Smith

There is an obvious retro element to this game, which is highlighted by the dark interface and atmospheric music. You have to crack a series of puzzles to progress and answers are rarely obvious – but the end result is a challenge that feels intriguing enough to keep you playing until you finish it.

**A quirky adventure game bolstered by a series of challenging puzzles.**

★★★★★

● Price **£2.49/$3.99**

# Luxuria Superbia

This game involves caressing a flower to watch it grow, but it is almost impossible to describe. You have to make certain movements within the main screen and then be rewarded by phrases and sounds, the ultimate goal is unclear. For originality it is brilliant and most people will get something from it, but you should be prepared to not analyse and just go with it.

**A highly unusual game that will likely grow on you over time.**

★★★★★

● Price **£2.99/$4.99**

# The Cave

This point-and-click adventure, reminiscent of The Secret of Monkey Island, features a compelling narrative with lashings of self-aware humour and entertaining puzzles. Don't let the tiny graphics put you off, because it moves with gusto, and the presentation and music have obviously been lavished with care.

**A masterful '90s-esque point-and-click adventure that is also intensely funny.**

★★★★★

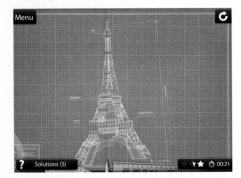

● Price £0.69/$0.99

# Blueprint 3D

 In this innovative game you have to move elements until they make up a visible, recognisable 3D image. While this might sound dull, it is actually quite challenging – but never stressful. It subtly makes you want to continuously progress. It's completely original and very well put together while still taxing your brain.

**A truly original app with the likelihood of a long-term appeal.**

★★★★★

● Price £2.99/$4.99

# Worms™ 3

 The vast majority of players - not just fans of the concept - will enjoy what is on offer in this version. It still feels like the classic, but with many extras included such as online multiplayer warfare. It offers a huge amount of flexible gameplay, resulting in a brilliant reinvention of a classic and well-loved game.

**A great game that keeps all of the Worms goodness in-tact.**

★★★★★

● Price £1.99/$2.99

# Pacific Rim

 The graphics in Pacific Rim are impressive, but the fighting mechanism needs improving. The monsters and gameplay are cleverly done, and it could be a monster-battling winner, but it's slow at times and the controls are iffy. Still, it offers enough for those who don't often play fighting games to enjoy it for a bit.

**Despite the name, it's just another fighting game with mediocre controls.**

★★★☆☆

● Price £2.99/$4.99

# The Room 2

## Contemplative and engaging, the room returns

 It starts with a room and a box but, just like the first offering, that is all that is needed to open up a world full of mystery, brain ache and sweaty palms. The Room 2 will get your heart thumping as you try and figure what is inside the objects.

It is akin to a point-and-click adventure game but located on specific objects that can be prodded and turned. Drawers can be pulled, locks can be revealed, buttons can be pressed, letters opened and read. It builds up into an intriguing puzzler that is now spread over multiple areas.

In some senses, this departure from the first game is not hugely welcome since it means you're having to pinch out to see the overall room before leaving to

another object, rather than spending time on one piece and getting to know all of its intricacies. But the good looks of the game and the atmosphere that is created makes it feel very real, so you don't mind exploring everything.

It helps too that there is a hint system so you don't ponder over the same puzzle for absolutely ages (unless you want to, of course). You don't run the risk of boredom either. The crafting of this game and the fun you'll have with it more than outweighs its relatively short playing time.

**An enormously immersive game that will hurt, tease and intrigue the brain as you while away a few hours.**

★★★★☆

■ You must discover every clue to succeed

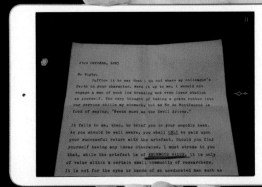

■ A simple puzzle to get you going, you just need to

● Price £2.99/$4.99

■ Even the maps that help you navigate Botanicula's labyrinthine world are beautifully stylised and well-presented

■ It's a weird and wonderful world amid the tree of Botanicula, populated by microscopic flora and all sorts of bizarre fauna

# Botanicula

## An intelligent point-and-click adventure

### PROS/CONS

▲ The art direction is strong and extremely well-explored

▲ The soundtrack could contend with triple-A game releases

▼ Price-to-content ratio is questionable

▼ Little replay value once you have completed puzzles

 Amanita Design has proven itself in the point-and-click genre with Machinarium, a playful and cerebral approach to drag-and-drop gameplay. With Botanicula, the company moves away from hand-drawn robotics into stylised design, combining 2D detail with unique atmospheric background art.

The production values on offer in the game are incredible. Amanita Designs is proving its expertise at maximising the potential of its chosen art direction. The studio takes the botanic style to creative conclusions that are both unique and familiar, evoking memories of the old LucasArts puzzle games that established the genre. Play it with headphones, too – you don't often get soundtracks this well produced anymore, and the beauty is in its detail.

Ported from the PC, Botanicula suits the iPad perfectly. Even the deceptively minute interactive objects respond to the touchscreen effectively, and the letterbox UI keeps the play area clear of anything that would otherwise detract from the art. This isn't a casual experience; like Machinarium before it, Botanicula is knowingly deceptive in its puzzles; everything is offered without an explanation, and it's a refreshing non-patronising puzzler for players that want to put a bit more time into their games.

That said, it's a short game. If you're a completionist that wants to tap everything on-screen to try and max out your collectibles (read: concept art), then Botanicula will take you no more than five hours. The price of admission is well worth the experience, but with little replayability and a core experience that holds up weakly on a second play, you're really going to want to invest yourself in the introspective, lateral thinking that will take you through Botanicula's levels.

**A gorgeous, well-polished puzzle game, demonstrating some of the best level design the genre has to offer, along with a great soundtrack.**

★★★★☆

## "You don't often get soundtracks this well produced anymore"

■ There are little experiences hidden around the game

# Creative

## Whatever you want to make, the iPad can help

"The iPad can be an easel, darkroom, recording studio and much more"

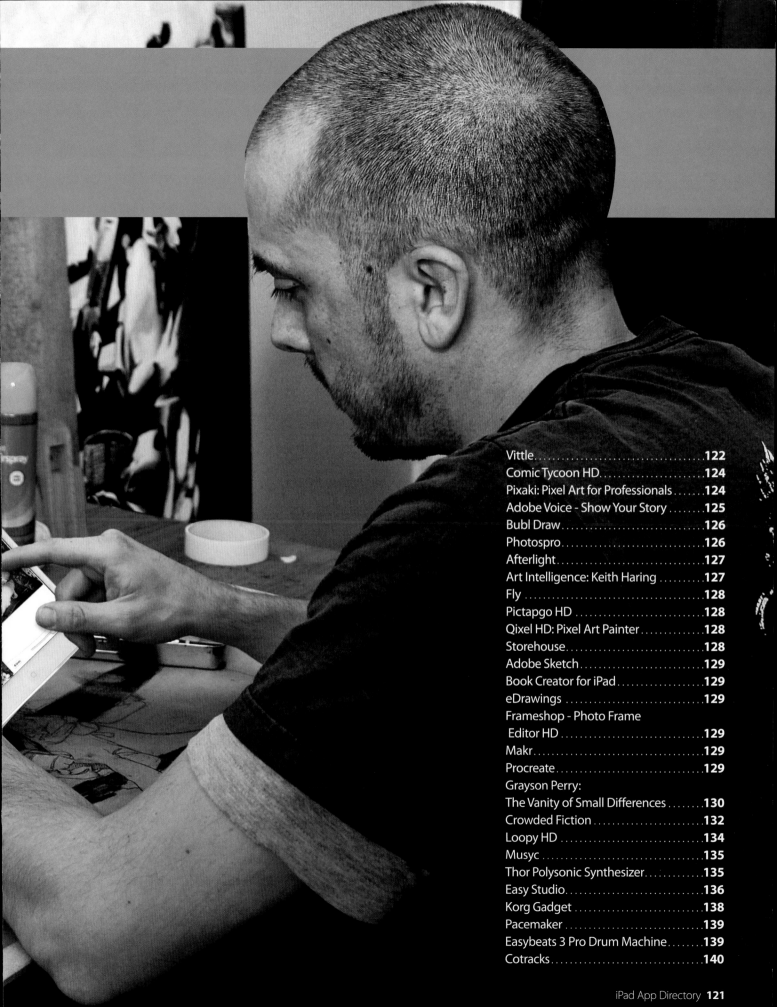

You can turn off the dancing dots and mute the microphone if you wish

Photographs can be pulled in from the camera roll and used in a project

● Price £5.99/$8.99

# Vittle

## For when pictures can say it better than words

 Vittle is effectively a whiteboard. But it is not just any whiteboard. It allows you to draw using a multitude of colours and the ability to include photographs from your Camera Roll, but it also lets you record what you are producing. By capturing your drawing, you are able to create videos that can then be played back. It enhances presentations, allows you to get points across clearly and even have a bit of simple fun.

The app is intended for serious use first and foremost although the interface is certainly not business-like. It is as user-friendly as you would hope most apps to be these days and so across the top, you have options to draw, erase, select, point and add as well as an assortment of colours and some recording facilities.

This intuitive nature allows for frivolous use as well and, indeed, the in-built video showcases the less serious uses for the app. You could create a video that spells out "I love you" and send it to your other half, for example. If you so wish, you could put it on YouTube or Vimeo immediately after you have recorded them. Videos can also be emailed or put up on company servers if you wish to use them in a presentation.

As well as being able to draw and add photos, you can include a voice over too. This will enable you to explain what you are doing as you are actually doing it. The recording facilities are simple enough to enable this. You tap Rec and then either Stop or Pause if you want to get your thought process into order or work on some magic in terms of how your video is seen by others people.

You are not confined to producing work on the one screen. As well as support for multiple projects, you can have multiple pages and scenes within them. By using different scenes, you are better able to edit later, moving them around, deleting and re-ordering so that you have the perfect end result. The length of the project is left entirely up to you as there are no limits, so you could go on for hours if you so wished.

As if to underline the business use, there is a PDF import option so that work from PowerPoint or Keynote can be added. There is a camera lock tool to let users smoothly pan the recorded view and there is a laser point tool if there is an image on the screen that you want to point to and record while giving your presentation. Videos are exported in 720p HD which is more

## "The intuitive nature allows for frivolous use as well, and, indeed, the in-built video showcases the less serious uses for the app"

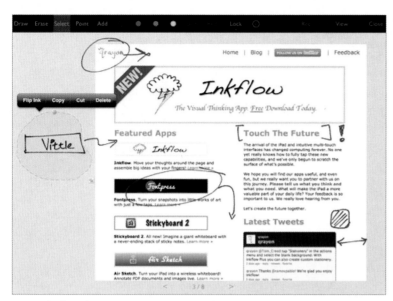

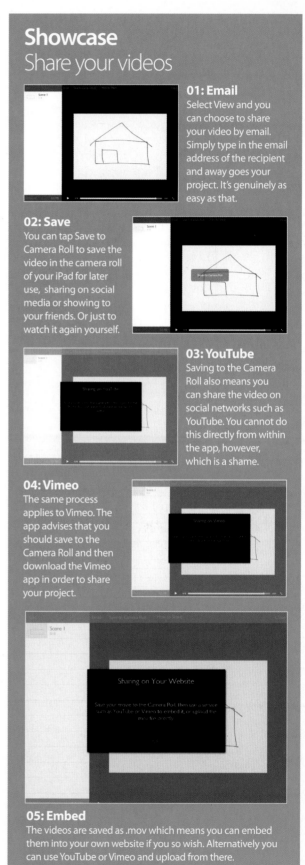

■ Record videos of you creating presentations and zoom in on key areas

than adequate and, even better, Vittle does not lay claim to anything you create. The introduction video also tells you that it would be interested to see what people come up with. It's an open-natured product that will allow for a lot of creative flourish.

There is a free version of the app should you want to try it before you plunge in and pay. You will see that you can quickly produce storyboards but only the full, paid-for version has the unlimited recording length, customisable colour palette and pen setting, camera lock, laser pointer and PDF import. You can only have single projects with the free version too.

Still, many people may find that more than adequate so it is worth downloading the free version to try out first. That said, the full version - if

you do decide to upgrade – is very much worth the asking price. We like the way it places those options at the top of the screen and keeps the actual main drawing screen as large and as uncluttered as it could ever hope to be. Menus do drop down into the drawing space but it's a temporary thing while you sort out and decide what you want, whether it be opacity or a thicker brush, for example.

The playback is also great. There is a little shimmering on the lines that you create which gives the presentations a lift and makes them appear more fun and less straight. It's like the effect you see in Rhubarb and Custard and it definitely makes it a lot more enjoyable to watch back.

Vittle is a fabulous app that is loaded with features and can really aid with both productivity as well as provide a bit of fun amongst friends. And in the end, what is the iPad for if not for improving productivity, interacting with friends, and having fun?

**An outstanding application for storyboarding that has a wide range of uses.**

★★★★★

■ A free version of the app is available to download from the App Store

## Showcase
### Share your videos

**01: Email**
Select View and you can choose to share your video by email. Simply type in the email address of the recipient and away goes your project. It's genuinely as easy as that.

**02: Save**
You can tap Save to Camera Roll to save the video in the camera roll of your iPad for later use, sharing on social media or showing to your friends. Or just to watch it again yourself.

**03: YouTube**
Saving to the Camera Roll also means you can share the video on social networks such as YouTube. You cannot do this directly from within the app, however, which is a shame.

**04: Vimeo**
The same process applies to Vimeo. The app advises that you should save to the Camera Roll and then download the Vimeo app in order to share your project.

**05: Embed**
The videos are saved as .mov which means you can embed them into your own website if you so wish. Alternatively you can use YouTube or Vimeo and upload from there.

● Price £2.99/$4.99

# Pixaki: Pixel Art for Professionals

## Blocky graphics rule the roost with this art package

■ The opacity of your art can be altered with the use of a simple slider

Pixel art appears to be one of those art forms that will never go out of fashion. It harks back to days gone by on home computers and consoles of the 8-bit and 16-bit eras of the Eighties and Nineties. Graphics back then were blocky and yet richly formed, but you can still see examples of it today as people attempt to 'go retro' and evoke memories.

Pixaki allows for the recreation of these gems with a touch interface that lets you manipulate chunky pixels on a canvas spreading up to 512px by 512px. It is amazing what you can come up with when you are using such a limited colour palette and you can let your imagination run free. The way Pixaki allows you to create graphics is invitingly easy. That said, Pixaki does not fall back on old methods, so it's not just a

simple case of filling in squares. The app has a contemporary edge to its creative approach, meaning that you can produce art consisting of over 20 layers and even control their opacity. You can also export them as Photoshop PSD or PNG files. You can copy and paste graphics and layers, customise the palette and zoom in with up to 400 times magnification.

On top of that, you can pop any graphics into Dropbox for easy porting. The beauty of Pixaki is that it allows anyone to be able to produce amazing pixel art, whether it's for a creative project or just for fun.

**Being able to produce your own personal pixel art is made fun and as easy as possible.**

★★★★★

● Price 1.49/$1.99

# Comic Tycoon HD

## Create your own comic strips using your photos, then share them

 Comics are still a very popular form of entertainment. Although some have fallen by the wayside in paper format, the iPad has given many others a new lease of life. They're creative and fun and combine stories with visuals. However, creating your own comic strips has traditionally relied on you being able to draw.

Step forward Comic Tycoon HD for the iPad, which lets you use your photographs to form the cells that form a typical strip. You can then 'cartoonise' these images, turning them into comic art, before adding all sorts of special effects – from captions to art.

The software is easy to get to grips with. As well as being able to take your own photos using the iPad camera, you can import images from your Photo Roll. Not everything is straightforward, however. We struggled to

scrap what we had already done and start afresh without leaving the app, and going back in and deleting various effects was not immediately obvious – try layers!

But when you get your head around these quirks, you find that you can very quickly produce a comic that you can then share via social media services such as Facebook or Twitter.

Comic Tycoon HD makes good use of the Retina screen of the newer iPads and allows for great flexibility in layout, ensuring that you can dive in, be creative and impress all of your readers.

**Fun and simple, it's hard not to enjoy creating your own comics and the artistic flair that this app allows.**

★★★★★

■ Each image is layered on top of each other as you set about building your comic strip

● Price Free

# Adobe Voice
## An easy way to create narrated slideshow videos

So, what's your story? Whatever message you want to relate, Adobe Voice makes it incredibly easy to do so in the form of an animated slideshow video with voice narration. It's so simple to pick up and use that even the tutorial is largely superfluous, and within minutes you'll have created your first, professional-looking video. Choose a preset structure, such as 'Promote an Idea' or 'Share an Invitation', and you'll be advised on what to put in each slide, but you can ignore this and do what you like, adding and removing slides. The editing is all done in portrait view, with the current slide preview in the middle, a strip of slide thumbnails along the bottom and context-sensitive options at the top. For each slide, you can choose a photo (your own or search for a Creative Commons image), icon (from over 25,000) or text. Or use one of the five layout options to combine these. Then you hold the mic button and record your commentary.

To style things up you can select one of 32 varied themes, which determine the background, colour scheme and text style. There's also a choice of background music, from the built-in jingles or your own library. While there's not really any scope for fine-tuning – things like font and text size are set automatically and layout choices are limited – there are enough creative options to make your project stand out. A quick peek at the Explore section showing other users' videos reveals Adobe Voice's versatility.

Once happy with your video, you can upload it to Adobe's servers and share a weblink for it via all the usual suspects like Facebook, Twitter, Email or Message. Sadly, there's no option to export it to use in other applications, but videos are stored locally in the Projects tab so you can view and re-edit them later as you wish.

---

**While it has some limitations, it makes it incredibly easy to create impressive, attractive slideshow videos**

★★★★★

> "Within minutes you'll have created your first, professional video"

■ Browse a gallery of videos created by others – there is a wide range of styles and topics

■ The use of the app is simple and intuitive - you'll be on your way in minutes

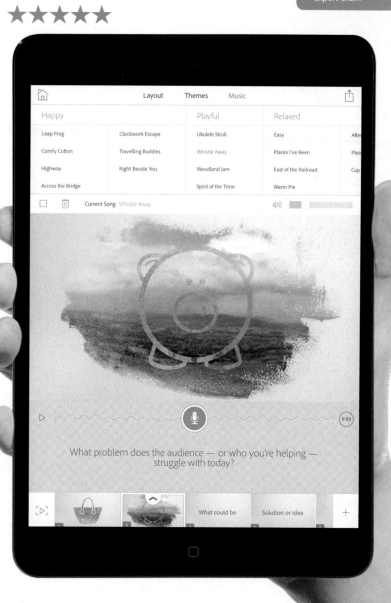

# Bubl Draw

## Tap, scribble and draw to create beautiful music

When it comes to making music on iPad, it doesn't have to be about beatpads, pro DJ mixing desks and virtual guitars. Bubl Draw offers something different because the screen is not only your instrument; it's also your interactive canvas.

Designed as an interactive development tool for young children, it's incredibly simple to use. But herein lies the brilliance. There are six 'instruments' to play with, but each one is actually a coloured brush that you can use. Tap one and you can paint on the screen. Draw lines, or join a line to itself to create a circle. Once they're on the page, you can tap the lines to add balls that move along them making sounds, or tap a circle to create a one-off sound. These sounds mix beautifully together, creating a

melody without any effort. There are three different soundboards, too, with each one offering a collection of instruments, beats, and sounds.

Each of these soundboards are different from each other, and mixing sounds is so much fun it's likely that you'll spend more time playing with the app than your kids. If you can bear to part with it, the app is perfect for youngsters; the bright colours, simple interface and immediate, melodic reward make it extremely easy to pick up and enjoy. Get Bubl Draw for your kids and you'll both fall in love with using it.

**Drawing and music merge in a lovely example of how to make music fun for young children.**

★★★★★

■ The results are often as colourful as they sound

■ Draw shapes on the screen, manipulate them or tap them to make music

---

● Price £1.49/$1.99

# Photospro

## Manage, share and collate your pictures

Google, Apple, Microsoft, Dropbox... everyone wants to take charge of the unsightly pile of photos we're shooting on our smartphones and tablets. No one's quite cracked the formula yet though, so you can't blame PixoMobile for

giving it a stab with PhotosPro. It does a decent job of showing you your recent pictures in an appealing grid-based interface, and there's an interesting map view that indicates exactly where each shot was taken. It's also possible to jump to other albums

besides the Camera Roll. Sharing one or more images is nice and straightforward too, via whatever third-party accounts you've hooked up to iOS — Twitter, Facebook, Flickr and Dropbox options are all here – and doing so only takes a few taps.

You can also build 'Stories', collections of text and images that tell the tale of a particular holiday or a day out — all of this is handled by a linked PixoMobile service called Pixotale. In many ways PhotosPro offers a superior experience to the rather basic iOS Photos app, but without any truly compelling features, it's not something we'll be repeatedly coming back to. On the other hand, if you find the integrated iOS photo experience frustrating, then a mere £1.50 is only a small price to pay for a replacement.

**An improvement on iOS Photos, but short on features that make it truly stand out.**

★★★★★

■ PhotosPro makes it easy to both browse your photos and share them with others

■ You can quickly pull up EXIF data for each image in your library

● Price £0.69/$0.99

# Afterlight

## Adjust your photos with this affordable editor

While no-one looks good taking a photo with their iPad, the tablet is great for editing your pictures. Afterlight is an affordable alternative to apps such as Photoshop Touch and includes a mixture of professional-quality adjustment tools (brightness, contrast, saturation, highlights, exposure, cropping are all here) and simpler Instagram-like filters, textures and borders. Almost all of these tools are controlled using sliders, which might sound overly simplistic, but are surprisingly exact. The photo filters are a little basic (with the best ones costing extra), however there are also unique 'guest filters' created by Instagram users. The scratched up texture effects and broad selection of borders are also quite impressive.

In addition to being able to share your touched-up photos to all of the usual social networks (Facebook, Twitter, Instagram, Flickr), you can also pay in-app to have them printed as postcards. This is a really nice touch and allows you to decorate your home – rather than your Facebook profile – with all of your favourite iPhone photos., so you can show off your photos on and off-screen.

**A brilliant alternative to more well-known photo editing apps, with ease of use and great sharing options.**

★★★★☆

● Price £3.99/$5.99

# Art Intelligence: Keith Haring

## See how the world affected Keith Haring and his work

Akin to a coffee table art book, Art Intelligence showcases the work of artist Keith Haring, showing his graffiti and paintings and highlighting his political messages. You can see them in isolation, view them in a timeline and read about what motivated him to produce those pieces. By the end you gain a greater appreciation of his art and the man himself.

While most people who buy this app will undoubtedly have heard of Mr Haring, the people who will get most out of it will be new to him. You get a wonderful glimpse into his life: whether it be his MTV era, the New York club scene or his sad death as a result of AIDS.

There are two other parts to the navigation. 'Connections' links the ideas so you can see at a glance how they all fit together. 'Conversations' allows you to converse and find out the impact his work has had on others. This is where an iPad app can exceed the traditional coffee table art book. Art Intelligence shows how such work can be displayed to near perfection and for the price, you'll have yourself an intellectual bargain. An essential for fans.

**Get more out of contemporary art and learn about the fascinating life and times of Keith Haring.**

★★★★☆

■ Explore Haring's art and the various moments that inspired him

■ Haring's work is presented in a beautiful timeline

 Creative

● Price Free

# Fly

## Edit multiple videos together on the fly!

■ Add clips to the editing stream with ease

■ Create epic videos in a matter of minutes

 Budding movie-makers will love playing around with this simple video-editing app as it really makes you feel as though you're conducting operations in the editing room and crafting your own masterpiece. You simply import movies from your Photos app or shoot them in-app and can view them in multiple windows at once to get the best feel of when to splice them together. You can trim and re-arrange clips, place pictures within pictures and much more.

However, many of the special effects that you will want to use, such as the option to import audio and use gesture editing, are only available as in-app purchases, so you'll have to be prepared to lay out quite a bit of cash to get the optimum experience. But at least this free version will allow you to get a

good feel for the app and its many features so that you are able to make an informed decision on whether to go for this instead of iMovie. The fact that Apple's movie-making app is totally free to iOS 8 users will probably tip the balance, though. Some neat touches and a slick interface at least make this a contender.

■ It's easy to edit videos on the go with this sleek and easy-to-use app

**We like the idea of super-fast video editing on the fly, but you'll have to pay out a lot to enjoy all of the features.**

★★★★★

● Price Free

# Storehouse - visual storytelling

 Storehouse is a clever app that lets you create stories using videos, images and text. The process is very simple and you'll surprise yourself with impressive creations. Gesture control is exceptional with simple swipes and zooming, and it comes together to create an effective sharing platform.

**A great idea that combines creative processes with simplicity.**

● Price £1.49/$1.99

# Qixel HD : Pixel Art Painter

 Qixel HD takes the simple premise of large pixels and turns them into a mechanism to create art in the most basic of ways, but with a lot of versatility. It is easy to use, no matter how much talent you have, and we found ourselves quickly creating likeable works. It also has potential for use in software design and for children to enjoy to keep boredom away.

**A unique and accessible art creation tool for most ages.**

● Price £1.99/$2.99

# Pictapgo HD

 This version of PicTapGo has been specially designed for the iPad, making the app a lot more practical. There are many filters included to spruce up your photos, and they include live previews, though as these features are available in other apps it isn't unique – but that does not stop it being a very competent photo editor and sharing tool.

**A highly competent photo editor that looks even better on this iPad version.**

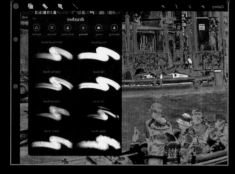

● Price £3.99/$5.99

# Procreate

Procreate beats the competition with its ability to create canvases of up to 4K pixels (Ultra HD), add countless layers, altering their type (eg darken) and opacity, and the huge selection of brushes, which can be fine-tuned. It even records your actions, which can be exported as a time-lapse video!

**Better than most apps of its kind, this is a creative powerhouse.**

★★★★★

● Price Free

# Adobe Sketch

For inspiration, Adobe Sketch is worth it as you get to see the works of fellow users. You will, however, need some serious talent to create distinctive sketches as the tools may feel limited for average user. The interface produces a clean, creative environment, but extra features would help.

**A well presented sketching app with some minor limitations in its tools.**

★★★★★

● Price Freemium

# Makr

Makr offers a unique approach to creating and learning. There are many design templates included and inspiration can be found in every corner. However, some of the designs can be quite difficult to fathom. Some tweaks are needed for this to be a real contender but the potential is definitely there.

**Lots of design potential, but the implementation could be more logical.**

★★★★★

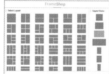
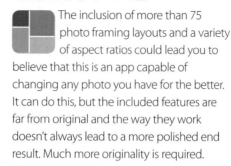

● Price £2.99/$4.99

# Book Creator for iPad

Book Creator is designed to let you build eBooks using images, text, videos and drawings. This is not necessarily a new idea, but the way it works helps to make it accessible to anyone and it cuts out most of the fiddly bits that make book creation problematic. It works best in education, but there is no reason why you cannot use it for fun and we admit to playing with it for far too long.

**A brilliant solution for creating personalised books.**

★★★★★

● Price £1.49/$1.99

# Frameshop - photo frame editor HD

The inclusion of more than 75 photo framing layouts and a variety of aspect ratios could lead you to believe that this is an app capable of changing any photo you have for the better. It can do this, but the included features are far from original and the way they work doesn't always lead to a more polished end result. Much more originality is required.

**A capable app, but also a somewhat uninspiring photo-editing solution.**

★★★☆☆

● Price £1.49/$1.99

# eDrawings

This app offers compatibility with many popular file types and you can also interact with each drawing. However, it can be difficult to use, and slow on some devices. Still, it's very ambitious and ahead of the technology it's for so the occasional performance quirk is acceptable. This could be a game-changer.

**Ambitious and tricky to use, but some people will absolutely love this app.**

★★★☆☆

■ There are two menu buttons that give you all of your options within the app

Andrea Mantegna (c.1430 - 1506)
*The Adoration of the Shepherds*, c.1450
Tempera on canvas, transferred from wood
Metropolitan Museum of Art, New York. Anonymous Gift, 1932.
Image copyright The Metropolitan Museum of Art/Art Resource/Scala, Florence

Mantegna was an early prodigy of the Italian Renaissance, and this work was painted when he was only in his early twenties. With meticulous attention to detail, he places the Virgin and Child in the centre of the composition, with Joseph asleep on their right. Behind is a fenced-in orchard symbolising her virginity. On the right are the adoring shepherds in their worn clothing and beyond is a mountainous landscape with a stark, single tree, which might be read as a prefiguring of the Cross on which Christ was later to die.

■ Users can also look up the historical references and the artwork they relate to

● Price £1.99/$2.99

# Grayson Perry: The Vanity of Small Differences

## The Turner Prize-winner has latest work turned into an intriguing download

The App Store is becoming a great place to be exposed to aspects of culture that you perhaps might not otherwise encounter. In recent years downloads have appeared that allow users to explore the finer mechanics of a classical orchestra, or embark on tours of Renaissance art galleries. Now we have this work by Turner Prize-winner Grayson Perry – a series of tapestries that take the user on a journey through the British class system, telling the story of a man called Tim Rakewell, a character inspired by another 18th Century work of art. The Vanity of Small Differences started life as a gallery

project, but has now embraced the mobile platform, with each of Perry's six pieces being captured in high-res images, meaning users can pinch-zoom right in and scrutinise the smallest details and subtleties of each tapestry.

Users can swipe between each piece as they wish, taking in the different aspects and working with the interactive touch points that cover each screen. These identify whether something in the tapestries refers to another artwork, and where the inspiration comes from. There are also more social comments about what that particular aspect of the piece is

showing, and how it fits into the overall theme of the class system in 21st Century Britain.

Getting right into the project as an app, The Vanity of Small Differences keeps things very simple when it comes to interface, with no main menu screen, just straight into the first tapestry. There is a menu button in the bottom-left corner of the screen that allows users to get more information about the work, as well as read up on the historical references that feature throughout. There is also a chance to see Perry's original sketchbook images and how each scene evolved over time. From within this menu screen there is a healthy dose of extra content to support the main event, the artwork itself, giving the more keen art eye plenty to look at.

But it's more than just your eyes that are required here as there is also an

"There is a healthy dose of extra content to support the main event, the artwork itself, giving the keen art eye plenty to look at"

The old aristocratic stag with its tattered tweed hide is being hunted down by the dogs of tax, social change, upkeep and fuel bills.

■ The artwork offers a sometimes surreal class commentary on life in modern Britain

audio commentary from Grayson Perry himself, discussing the finer points of each piece and the reasoning behind some of the details. It's a great touch as listening to Perry soon feels like you're being accompanied around the exhibit by the artist himself, something that any art lover would revel in as an experience. This narrative tour sees you and Perry follow the lead character of the tapestry through his class journey, Perry discusses inspirations, locations and even the origin of the name for the work, giving a further window into his world.

When you're moving through this section of the app you do feel as if there is plenty of content to discover and things to take in, what with the near relentless references to historical art pieces and the deep arguments

around class and taste in Britain. However, this feeling doesn't last, and the content does run out quicker than you expect. The four sections of the main tab don't take long to browse through, and though it's nice to be able to come back at any time and admire the tapestries as though they were artwork in your own home, there is a sense that the app is missing something beyond the artwork.

This is more noticeable when you consider what some developers have done with apps like The Orchestra, where a niche subject area has been opened up. The Vanity of Small Differences is accessible, but there may be moments when you feel out of your depth with some of the references.

Nothing should stop you from downloading this app however, it's well-priced, comments on the state of British society and above all contains artwork that you'll be glad you were able to appreciate, interact with and show to others on your device.

**A niche app yes, but art lovers aren't the only ones who can appreciate the talent in this app.**

■ This is an app that will most likely be something different to your usual download

### 01: Tapestries
The star of the show, the six tapestries that form The Vanity of Small Differences are available by swiping across your screen, and each one can be zoomed in on.

### 02: Touch points
Each piece is also covered with a host of interactive hotspots, where you can find out more about an item or feature of the scene. There are text and audio notes.

### 03: Audio
Opt to take the audio tour, and you will be walked through the 'class journey' of the app by the artist himself, Grayson Perry. It's an informative addition to the app.

### 04: Text
Tapping the Menu icon accesses a range of accompanying texts. This includes explanations of some of the artistic references as well a biography of the artist.

### 05: Sketchbook
Further insight can be gained through the original sketches of each tapestry, complete with original handwritten notes from Perry, giving an idea of their origins.

■ The swiping controls are easy to use allowing you to pause and break wherever necessary

■ Taps and other movements are required to move the story along

● Price Freemium

# Crowded Fiction

## The humble word has a new lease of life

### PROS/CONS

▲ Reimagines how books are read

▲ Crowdsourcing helps create a community

▼ Crowdsourcing helps create a community

▼ The interface is perhaps too simple

 One of the unsung heroes of childhood was the Choose Your Own Adventure book series that placed readers in the shoes of a story's central character and asked them to make the key decisions. It was immersive and wonderfully engaging, bringing an extra dimension to good old-fashioned reading and inspiring entirely new ways to tell stories. Crowded Fiction takes this concept

and gives it a modern twist. The end product of a Kickstarter project, the app is an eBook reader where the stories come to life unlike any other eBook currently on the market. Before starting, users must choose a reading speed that's comfortable as the text moves across the screen. The text then spills across the display, bringing with it a sense of drama that usually requires some active imagination from the reader. Not any more, Crowded Fiction drops the user right into the heart of the story, where the decisions taken by on-screen gestures and the timing of those actions have a direct impact.

As the text plays, there are trigger moments and prompts within the narrative that require an action from the user. However, this is unlike the stop-start type of interactive books that are a staple on the App Store, where the user waits until a pause in the story to tap and swipe. 'Jackson's Choice', the debut story in Crowded Fiction sees the interactions take place 'live'

– as the events unfold and the words appear. The eBook tells the story of an art journalist who gets caught up in a murder case; as a result the user has to throw punches in fights by swiping the screen and navigate car chases by steering and tilting the device.

Every action has a consequence, so mistiming moves can land journalist Jackson in more trouble. To add to the tension most interactions involve alternating text where readers must try and tap the right option before it vanishes. It all feels very much like a video game, and indeed developers Vidya Gamer seem to have been heavily influenced by the gaming world, and have tried to bring elements of that level of immersion to reading in this app.

There are also conversations that require reading body language and speech to decide on a route to take and get the necessary information. To make this interaction worthwhile, Crowded Fiction is full of

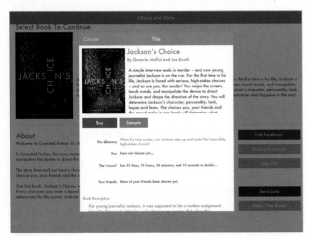

■ Jackson's Choice is the only book on offer for now, but there are more coming in this series alone

*---swipe to your LEFT---*

*Great! Next we will calibrate your natural reading speed. Your current reading speed is 30 characters per second. Adjust until it feels natural for you.*

*---swipe RIGHT to increase, swipe LEFT to decrease, or swipe UP/DOWN to keep---*

*---reading speed increased to 35 characters per second---*

*---RIGHT to increase, LEFT to decrease, or UP/DOWN skips---*

*---reading speed increased to 40 characters per second---*

*---RIGHT to increase, LEFT to decrease, or UP/DOWN skips---*

■ The app optimises for your own abilities and preferences using swipe controls

# "Every action has a consequence, so mis-timing moves can land journalist Jackson in more trouble"

achievements. Whether it's for how a situation is approached, or for taking the time to search a corpse properly, messages let users know immediately when one has been unlocked.

These achievements can be shared on Facebook, and readers can compare their own path with that of their friends, with every choice made by every reader being logged in Crowded Fiction's servers. The majority results will then be analysed and shape the next book in the series – essentially crowdsourcing Jackson's traits for future instalments of the narrative. In order to get access to the full book

an in-app purchase is required, but Crowded Fiction does allow users to sample the first seven chapters for free, and this is more than enough time to have anyone properly hooked to the exhilarating story, so parting with some money for the full version doesn't feel remotely grating.

Crowded Fiction is a unique experience, yet keeps the interface and functionality very simple for the user. Apart from the gesture box, it is just simple black text on white pages – and yet because of everything else going on in the app it feels very far from being two-dimensional.

For the commute or reading in bed, the one-of-a-kind experience gained from downloading and experiencing Crowded Fiction is one that is likely to leave a mark.

**This app has created a format that could change the genre on the digital platform.**

■ At first glance, this may look like a normal e-reading app, but this is much more

## Showcase
## Interactivity in Crowded Fiction

### 01: Prompts
Some words within the text are in bold, and tapped to cue some sort of interaction within the story. It can be anything from opening a door to searching a dead body.

### 02: Colours
There are also the coloured words, these are timing focused and the aim is to tap them when they turn green. This emphasises the right moment to carry out a specific action.

### 03: Swipe area
There are occasions where the reader can choose the direction in which Jackson goes, and swiping in a direction will send him off that way, or have him look around.

### 04 :Tilt
One scene in the book involves a car chase, and in order to get through it there's some tilt-control work to be done so that you barge another car off the road and get away.

### 05: Achievements
There are video game-like achievements to collect throughout the chapters too. These come from talking people round, searching bodies and other in-story feats.

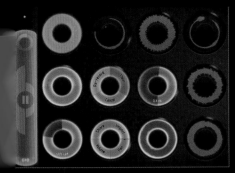

A customisable interface means that it is easy for users to get the settings just right

Audiobus means you can record from apps like djay 2 straight into Loopy HD

Price £2.49/$3.99

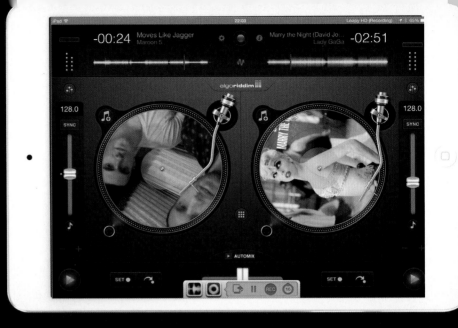

# Loopy HD

## You can make a mash-up in minutes by chaining apps together or recording live

This stylish, smartly designed app brings music creation to novices but tucks away sets of advanced options for the professionals. It's widely acclaimed, has attracted celebrities like Jimmy Fallon and Dub Fx, and basically lets you record short loops and then set them spinning on your screen.

Loopy HD has an intuitive enough interface, though to get the kind of precision you want will take a fair while as you become accustomed to the app. It's based around gesture-controls, so you flick the orange menu bar across to access settings like the timing section, where you then slide the tempo into place or tap out a beat to use as a metronome. You can set the metronome ticking or go with flashing lights instead, and set a count-in along with the length of a recording. Tap to start and stop recording, or to play and mute the loops once they're in place.

Record a few loops and then you can long-press to access volume, pan and more controls. If you happen to mess up your timing, you can twist the dials to set their start positions. However, if you get carried away and record for too long, the lack of a trim option soon stands out. Slide out the main panel and you can delve deep into the track settings, right down to options like

synchronisation controls, your playback and app settings. The controls are precise, so live artists and those familiar with music creation software will appreciate this app as much the casual user. Inter-app audio compatibility also means that Loopy HD can work as an input or output track through Audiobus. So you can record from djay 2 directly into Loopy HD, build up a textured loops mash-up and then, once you have everything in place, import it into GarageBand. It's a perfect way to create music on your iPad, and guaranteed to awaken your creativity.

**Loopy HD has the winning combination of being well-designed, fully-featured and fun; this app is definitely worth your money.**

★★★★★

"Those familiar with music creation software will appreciate this app as much as the casual user"

All you need is a sense of rhythm to start playing with loops

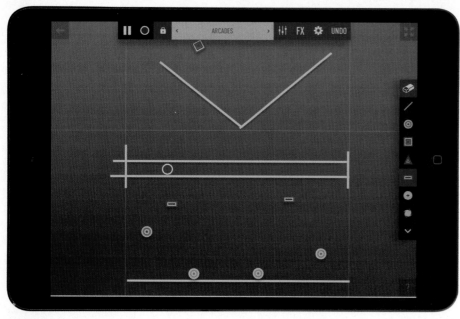

● Price Free

# Musyc

## Music making and great visuals come together

Musyc isn't as serious as some of the music creation available, but there is plenty of intelligence hidden within the initially casual feeling of this app. The basic premise is to create environments by using the line tool and drop in different shapes, each one presenting a different style of sound. The way you drop in each shape directly [...] rhythm. Drop somet[...] and it will keep that n[...] bounce, registering a [...] makes contact with a s[...]

The position it lands in also affects the note that is played, and this is before users can begin to play around with each shape, editing the sound in the mixer settings. The scope for creativity is huge as you can start a new song with a near-blank screen, as well as edit the app's pre-exisiting templates.

Though its more fun experimentation than serious creation, the app allows you to record and export your sounds to Dropbox, SoundCloud and your iTunes folder.

It's enormous fun to explore the app's various sounds, and to top it all off, it's visually appealing, too.

**A wonderfully engaging and easy-to-use music creation app with seemingly endless possibilities.**

★★★★★

● Price £10.49/$14.99

# Thor Polysonic Synthesizer

## A faithful recreation of Reason's legendary synth

If you want to go beyond the basics and create your own sounds, have a look at Propellerhead Software's Thor Polysonic Synthesizer, named after the Norse God.

There are three screens consisting of keyboard, knobs and routing. The first lets you play and there are useful features like the Assist button to choose a chord and Collapse, which reduces the keyboard to show only those notes. Latch Keys holds down keys and Strum lets you select several keys and play arpeggios by swiping.

The knobs screen is in three parts, each of which can be expanded and collapsed. Here you create your sound and the range of options is superb. There are six oscillator types consisting of analogue, wavetable, phase modulation, multi-oscillator and noise, and three slots. There are five filter types and three slots. You can play around for hours mimicking your favourite tracks.

A sound bank has 1,000 Thor patches from artists and sound designers, audio-in-background plays while using other apps, there's MIDI in, and more. It is rare that version one of anything is so good.

**It is not cheap, but then this is a professional music tool with an amazing array of features.**

★★★★☆

■ The knobs screen is where you can get creative

■ Assist on the left, Latch Keys and Strum on the right are all useful aids

■ The early levels advance you from geometric shapes to more complicated forms

■ The Expert mode gives you a blank canvas and all the tool for your animations

● Price £7.99/$11.99

# Easy Studio – Animate with Shapes!

## This fun and creative download offers animation for all ages

 If either you or your children are interested in creating cartoons, but think animation software looks too complicated, think again. Easy Studio – Animate with Shapes! offers an introduction to animating with simplified controls to help ages 6 to 106 get to grips with the art form.

Creating your first video is as easy as dragging and dropping shapes that resemble crate paper or fuzzy felt into positions on a blackboard-like background. Tap the camera icon on the sidebar to snap a still image, rearrange the shapes you want to animate into another position, tap the camera again, and repeat until

you have completed your intended animation. Press the triangular Play icon to watch an endless video loop of your handiwork.

Keen-eyed app lovers will note the shapes in Easy Studio resemble Montessori Geometry, which was created by the same developer, Les Trois Elles. This developer has lots of experience with interactive apps for Montessori Education, including teaching aids for basic number skills and speakingFrench. They have struck out on their own to produce Easy Studio, but have learnt a few lessons in educating themselves.

Starting out in Easy mode, you advance through five levels of growing

complexity and creative freedom. This begins with making simple geometric shapes to move around the screen, and advances to creating a model aeroplane that flies across a sky, complete with streaking clouds in the background.

Guidelines, which don't appear in the finished video, help users to know where to move shapes to next in the sequence through four of the five levels. Every time you press the camera icon, these guides will then move into the next position. While these magically appearing guidelines are fairly self-explanatory for first-time users, we suggest some parental supervision may be required for younger animators. The fifth and final level in Easy mode is a blank canvas for you to unleash your imagination and create your own masterpiece.

As you or your child's skills develop, you can switch to Expert mode. Here

*"The final level provides you with a blank canvas for you to unleash your imagination and create your own masterpiece"*

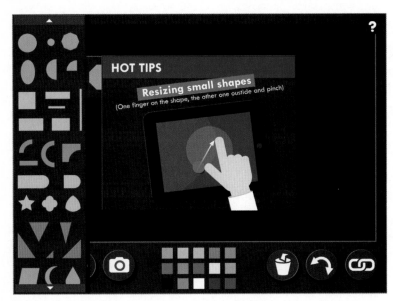

Gesture controls make it easy to resize, copy and group objects with just a few taps

you not only have a blank canvas with which to create, you also have a larger range of shapes to use as well as additional tools. Most significantly, you can now edit scenes either by modifying them or deleting them (though sadly you can't rearrange scenes). Other tools include templates for how shapes can be arranged into more complicated forms, such as birds, cars and human faces. You can also change the background colour and colour of individual shapes. Expert mode also introduces a range of really impressive gesture controls to further aid your animations. For example, a few deft moves with two fingers can select multiple shapes at once, copy and paste them, resize them or layer shapes on top of one another. This is the real benefit of Easy Studio: as your child develops so does the app, until they reach a point where they can generate hours of entertainment by themselves.

On the other hand, adult users may reach a limit sooner rather than later. As some of the videos produced with the app by the developers and included for free in the Library section show, the child-friendly shapes can be layered and rotated into some incredible forms,

which make for amusing videos. But this aesthetic isn't for everyone and it's hardly professional. Easy Studio can be considered a primer for those wanting to master the basics of stop motion, but they might want to download apps such as Animation Studio, Animation Desk for iPad and Animation Creator HD once they are ready to take their work to the next level.

All videos created can then be saved in-app and – obviously dependent on length and complexity – don't take up much space. For example, one of the templated videos from Easy mode takes up just 13.6KB, meaning that even if your child creates literally hundreds of animations, you can save them all to even the lowest storage capacity iPad.

The app has also been updated so that you can now export your animations to Camera Roll. From here you can share them on social media, the modern equivalent of displaying your children's painting on the fridge.

**Enjoyable for the whole family, Easy Studio teaches you how to master stop-motion animation.**

## Showcase
### Develop skills with Easy Studio

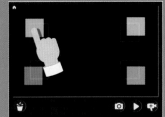

**01: The Tutorial**
The app opens in a sandbox level that acquaints you with the basic interface of dragging shapes into guidelines and using the camera button to snap scenes.

**02: Geometrics**
The next few levels show you how to create stop-motion projects by using basic shapes such as squares and triangles and arranging them into patterns.

**03: Cartoons**
As you advance through Easy mode, the animations become more complicated – combining shapes to make more complicated figures, such as this aeroplane.

**04: Blank canvas**
Once you've completed Easy mode, Expert mode provides a blank canvas to create whatever you can imagine with a range of more advanced tools to help achieve it.

**05: Library**
Every video you create can be saved and watched in the Library. From here you can also edit your animations, rearranging shapes in scenes or deleting scenes entirely.

## Creative

● Price £27.49/£38.99

# KORG Gadget

## Make music in a range of high-quality miniature touchscreen synths

KORG Gadget is billed as the ultimate mobile synth collection on your iPad, and the all-in-one music production studio. Surprisingly, despite this being an app that runs on a touchscreen tablet, these boasts aren't much of an oversell. Gadget really is an ambitious and hugely capable app, more than suitable for sketching out ideas and even creating complete songs. The app works in portrait, and the screen is split in half. In the app's main screen, the top is reserved for arranging your song, utilising an intuitive scene/loop system. The lower half of the screen is a typical mixer, with sliders and panning knobs. When inside a synth, you get access to a piano roll, for writing down notes, and the synth itself. Each of the 15 synths comes with a slew of presets, but it's perhaps more fun to start with the default sound and build your own.

Perhaps the most impressive thing about Gadget is how intuitive everything is. If you've used any sequencers before, you'll be right at home, but the depth in the app will soon find you immersed, eking out increasingly rich textures and sounds. Completed songs can be mixed down to Dropbox or uploaded to GadgetCloud, the app's Soundcloud-powered social network.

There are some minor niggles. Anything less than a fourth-generation iPad will struggle, effects are limited,

and there's no single-track export, limiting taking your Gadget songs elsewhere for mastering. However, KORG has promised to iterate on its product, and the 1.0.2 update already brought a number of interface changes that made the app more efficient and pleasurable to use. In short, Gadget is highly capable, highly impressive, and highly recommended.

**A must-have app for anyone remotely serious about creating electronic music. Great sounds and excellent features.**

★★★★★

### PROS/CONS

▲ Excellent range of sounds – there's 15 synths onboard

▲ Intuitive piano roll and arrangement tools create a perfect workspace

▼ Weak export options beyond mix-downs

▼ Effects are very limited and heavily dance orientated

## "An ambitious and hugely capable app, suitable for creating complete songs"

■ You can listen to other users' creations on GadgetCloud, which is similar to Soundcloud

■ The Choose Gadget screen is an overview of each synth's capabilities and characteristics

● Price Freemium

# Pacemaker

## Spotify-powered DJ app offers endless remixing

 Pacemaker for iPad is looking to turn the tables on premium DJ tablet apps with Spotify integration and a pick-and-mix way of selling effects.

Being the only DJ app that works with Spotify is a major hook, giving users access to 20 million tracks – but there are caveats. As well as requiring a Spotify subscription, you can't record or share remixes you make from the streaming service. However, Pacemaker works with iTunes, so you can record music you own, even offline.

On top of that, the app's colourful turntable interface looks amazing. Its gesture controls are highly intuitive and multitouch, so you can mix two tracks at once – but this could benefit from a tutorial for beginners. Professional users, however, might complain that you only have two channels and can't cue up more than one track at a time.

Something users might resent is that the only effect not behind a paywall is an adjustable equaliser – looping, echo, reverb and other effects are sold separately. However, Pacemaker approaches in-app purchases well, with detailed descriptions and a try-before-you-buy option.

**A DJ app for enthusiasts rather than pros, but it has potential as well as extra effects via in-app purchases.**

★★★★☆

---

● Price £2.99/$4.99

# EasyBeats 3 Pro Drum Machine

## An impressive beats creator

GarageBand is the obvious choice for making music, but there are many other apps that can be useful too. EasyBeats 3 Pro Drum Machine is worth adding to your collection and is designed to enable you to create beats easily. A four by four grid of sample pads is displayed and one of several built-in drum kits can be selected. It is also possible to import your own or online sound samples using iTunes' file import/export facilities.

You tap the sample pads to the beat of a metronome to record a loop-able bar. There are 16 bars, each up to 64-step quantised. A pattern editor enables you tap, copy and paste to tweak them and it is

really easy to use – it even supports pinch and spread to zoom in and out. Tap and hold a sample pad and you can modify the sounds, customising the high pass, reverb, distortion and other effects.

Your beats can be copied to the clipboard and pasted into GarageBand, meaning you can use your custom beat in your songs. EasyBeats is more fun than professional, but v3 improves on earlier versions and it's a great download.

**Let your creativity loose and build great beats for use in any of your (Garageband) music projects.**

★★★★★

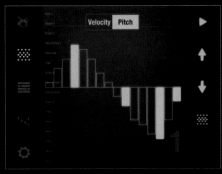

■ Pads can be edited to represent any drum sound

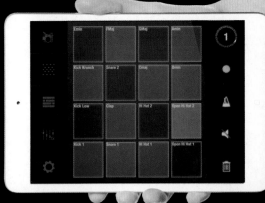

■ Not just a pretty interface, the app packs a hefty technical punch too

■ The touch pads make for great fun. Users can create beats, and also work on pre-existing ones

■ Each section can support up to three tracks, (12 in total), and each can be assigned a specific instrument

● Price £2.99/$4.99

# Cotracks

## Get collaborative with your friends while making music on a single iPad

### PROS/CONS

▲ Brilliant collaborative workspace for up to four users

▲ The range of sounds and tweaks is truly impressive

▼ Takes some time to learn all the controls

▼ Can get a little crowded with four around an iPad

Apps like GarageBand have meant the iPad is now an accepted part of the music making and producing process for amateurs and professionals alike. A quick glance at the Music section of the App Store and Google Play shows just how big a market this has become, as fully fledged professional software at high-end prices sit alongside free apps – all offering varying ranges of creative power and inspiration.

Cotracks by Futucraft is the latest app to show up on the radar, and the reason for that is the app's big focus on collaboration – in particular the possibility of up to four people getting creative on the same device. Cotracks'

biggest strength is its interface, which can be adapted in a single tap to suit single, dual or four-person usage on one device. Combined with the support of multitouch gestures, it means that an entire group of friends, or indeed a band, can gather around a single device and all get creative without being disrupted by others. The app can handle as many taps and swipes as four sets of hands can throw at it, and it means that a unique creative session can start up at any point and there is a great feeling of freedom that comes with that.

The single-person mode has a vertical interface with four sections of touch input on offer, each one able

to handle three tracks, and each layer one of three main instruments – two synths and a drum pad. Each one of these instruments has various types to choose from, differing in sound hugely, so there is no shortage of choice and variation when it come to finding a great sound.

In each of the four sections users can customise the look and sound of everything, with touch controls to tweak pitch, create a loop or sequence as well as alter the layout of the touchpad used to create a beat. It's impressively customisable, and it means that whether it's one user or four, everyone who's interacting with Cotracks can be completely comfortable and in control.

When it comes to the collaborative nature of the interface things are incredibly smooth. In single user mode, the third section down houses a button labelled Sessions; directly

## "Cotracks can handle as many taps and swipes as four sets of hands can throw at it, so a creative session can start at any point"

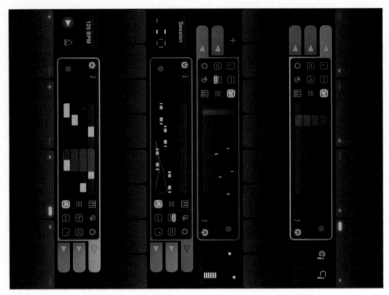

■ Gesture controls make it easy to resize, copy and group objects with just a few taps

below this is a set of three buttons, and from here the screen can be adjusted effortlessly depending on how many users are involved. Two-person view spins around two sections to face the opposite way, so a second user at the other end of the iPad can being editing. Tap the four-person option and each of the four sections jump out to face a side of the device, making it easy for four people to huddle over the device and get creating individually yet still working together.

Having everyone working in the same space makes it very easy to come together and share sequences and loops that are created. Users can drag and drop sequences from one window to another should they want to get exactly in time with someone else in the app. What this collaboration setup

also allows is the possibility of users with different sets of skills working together. For example, the musician of a group of friends could put together a sequence before handing it over to a novice, who can then put a creative stamp on it by tweaking effects and other aspects. Cotracks offers the chance for everyone to be equal and that potential is very powerful in an area of the App Store that while very diverse, can still feel niche to those without much musical talent but still want to get involved.

This highly-accessible app offers that opportunity, and the fact that it can be done on a single device makes it a great alternative to GarageBand jamming sessions. This is an entertainment app that regardless of musical ability, users will get a great kick out of, especially if used by a group huddled over a single device, throwing sequences around and getting creative in an intuitive space that has some unique sounds in its menu options.

**A truly great platform for creation that has hit upon a clever collaborative setup.**

★★★★★

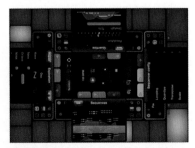

■ The collaborative set up uses all four sides of the device so that it is easily accessed

# Showcase
## Get collaborative in Cotracks

### 01: Single mode
When it's just you, Cotracks has a simple, stacked interface, with each of the four sections supporting three tracks. It's possible to tweak these as you like.

### 02: Double up
A single tap makes the interface more social. In the third section down, beneath the session button, is a row of three buttons, the middle one shifting it to two-person mode.

### 03: Group jamming
Cotracks can handle up to four at a time working with the app. Tap the furthest right interface button and everyone is designated a side of the device

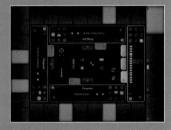

### 04: Multiple touches
There is complete freedom for each user because Cotracks handles the multiple touches easily. This means creativity and good fun too.

### 05: Export
Once everyone is happy, use the export options to get the sessions out there. The app links with iTunes, and you can export individual tracks from within the piece too.

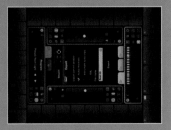

# Index

## Your at-a-glance guide to what's inside…

## Games

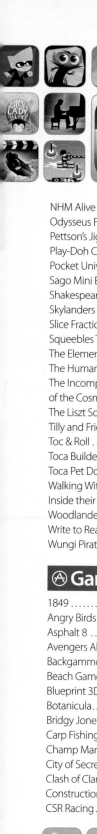

## Creative

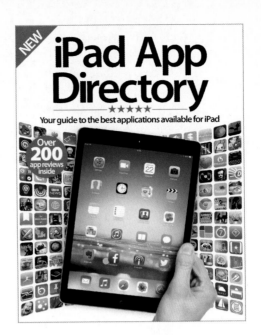

NEW

# iPad App Directory

★★★★★

Your guide to the best applications available for iPad

Over 200 app reviews inside

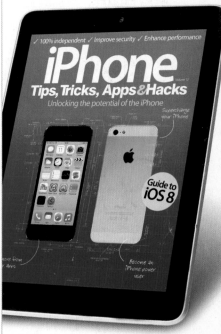